Energy and Urban Built Form

Edited by

Dean Hawkes, Janet Owers, Peter Rickaby and Philip Steadman

Centre for Configurational Studies
Design Discipline, The Open University

The Martin Centre for Architectural and Urban Studies
Department of Architecture, University of Cambridge

Butterworths
London   Boston   Durban   Singapore   Sydney   Toronto   Wellington

First published 1987

© Centre for Configurational Studies, Open University/Martin Centre for Architectural and Urban Studies, University of Cambridge, 1987

British Library Cataloguing in Publication Data

Energy and urban built form.
   1. Architecture and energy conservation.
   I. Hawkes, Dean   II. Martin Centre for Architectural and Urban Studies   III. Open University. *Design Discipline. Centre for Configurational Studies*
   696   NA2542.3

   ISBN 0–408–00891–1

Library of Congress Cataloging-in-Publication Data

Energy and urban built form

Papers presented at the International Seminar on Urban Built Form and Energy Analysis, held June 26–27, 1986, Darwin College, Cambridge, sponsored by Centre for Configurational Studies, the Open University and the Martin Centre for Architectural and Urban Studies.
     1. Power resources—Congresses.   2. Energy conservation—Congresses.   3. City planning—Congresses. 504 Includes bibliographies
I. Hawkes, Dean.   II. International Seminar on Urban Built Form and Energy Analysis (1986: Darwin College).   III. Open University. Centre for Configurational Studies.   IV. Martin Centre for Architectural and Urban Studies.
   TJ163.15.E525   1987   333.79   87–11640

   ISBN 0–408–00891–1

Printed and bound in England by
Anchor-Brendon Ltd., Tiptree, Essex

PREFACE

The papers which appear in this book were presented at the International Seminar on Urban Built Form and Energy Analysis, held at Darwin College, Cambridge, on 26th and 27th June, 1986.

The subject of the seminar was energy use in the built environment at a scale intermediate between individual buildings and cities. Research is well established at both the building scale and the urban scale, but comparatively little work has been done at the intermediate scale, where urban and architectural factors interact. Future urban development in configurations appropriate to energy efficient urban transport and servicing will require systematic knowledge of possible urban built forms and their properties. Recent research in this area has arisen from both buildings energy analysis and urban land use and transport modelling; it deals with the representation of urban built form, and with the simulation, prediction and optimization of its performance. Issues of interest include insolation and shading, thermal properties, occupancy patterns, interactions between uses, thermal upgrading and retrofitting, and the use of local heating systems.

The aim of the seminar was to consolidate and catalyse this emerging body of research by bringing together the small number of researchers already in the field or associated with it. The seminar was focused on the simulation and analysis of the performance of groups of buildings - city blocks, mixed-use urban developments, industrial developments, housing estates, and stocks of buildings such as houses and schools.

The idea for a seminar on this topic was originally conceived by Peter Rickaby. The seminar was organized by Peter Rickaby, Dean Hawkes, Janet Owers and Philip Steadman on behalf of the Centre for Configurational Studies at The Open University and the Martin Centre for Architectural and Urban Studies at the University of Cambridge. The seminar assistant was Helena Webster. Financial support was provided by the Science and Engineering Research Council, the Centre for Configurational Studies, The Martin Centre for Architectural and Urban Studies, and by the Design Discipline and the Faculty of Technology at The Open University.

This publication was designed and sub-edited by Janet Owers. The drawings were adapted for publication by Helen Mulligan. The contribution from Sergio Los was translated by Sue Chapman and Philip Steadman, and the camera-ready typescripts were prepared by Shirley Seal.

CONTENTS

INTRODUCTION

Dean Hawkes

"Organisms, societies, human persons, not least, cities, are delicate devices for regulating energy and putting it to the service of life.

The chief function of the city is to convert power into form, energy into culture, dead matter into the living symbols of art, biological reproduction into social creativity."

Lewis Mumford, *The City in History*

It may, at first sight, appear that the contents of this book are far removed from the concerns expressed by Mumford's passionate polemic. The majority of the papers gathered here present descriptions of techniques for calculating, and, hence minimizing, the energy consumption of groups of buildings, cities or entire regions. In *Part 1, the Region, the City and the Block*, the first three papers, by de la Barra and Rickaby, Matthews, and Rickaby, all present descriptions of mathematical models. Similarly, in *Part 2, Housing and Building Groups*, Fergusson and Barrett, Steadman and Brown, and Dupagne discuss approaches to the computation of the energy demand or energy-related properties of housing designs or groups of buildings, and Penz and Gupta both concentrate upon quantitative matters. In *Part 3, Policy and Planning*, the attention shifts to questions of the politics of energy and the built environment with Owens asking some fundamental questions and Sheldrick and Cooper exploring the mechanisms by which technical developments may be translated into effective action.

All of this is a reflection of the specific significance which the subject of energy has assumed in industrialized society, since the shock of oil price inflation in the early 1970s, and sustained well into the 80s by the anxieties which are provoked by events like the Chernobyl disaster. In the light of these events it is demonstrably prudent to seek ways by which levels of energy consumption may be reduced in order to maintain the institutions of society, and tools for analysis have an important part to play in this process. Of all of these institutions it is the city - with its surrounding region - which consumes the overwhelming proportion of the total energy used, in its aggregation of buildings for all purposes, and in the process of communications between them.

In his wide-ranging paper Los argues for the restoration of a sense of historical continuity and contextual response in an architecture which is also efficient in its use of energy. The projects described in *Part 4, Case Studies*, by Hawkes and Baker and Wagner, may be seen as specific instances of this general proposition. They also show how tools of analysis and technical knowledge may be used in the production of such designs.

Writing in 1961 Mumford was clearly using *energy* in a much broader definition than is implied in the work presented here, but his relationships of *power* and *form*, and *energy* and *culture* apply as powerfully to this discussion as in his wider meaning. Technical knowledge is of little value if its use is limited to purely technical ends. The city of the future has, for its very survival, to become more energy-efficient than the megalopolis of the mid-twentieth century. Mumford's definition of the city as a 'delicate device' in which energy is put to the service of life serves as a reminder of our responsibilities and of the potential of the low-energy city.

PART 1   THE REGION, THE CITY AND THE CITY BLOCK

A HIERARCHICAL LAND USE AND TRANSPORT MODEL FOR ENERGY EVALUATION

Tomas de la Barra

Instituto de Urbanismo
Universidad Central de Venezuela

Peter A. Rickaby

Centre for Configurational Studies
The Open University

Abstract

The purpose of the model described here is to assist the comparative evaluation of urban and regional settlement patterns from the point of view of energy use. In order to achieve this, the model must be able to simulate the use of land and transport for various purposes, and make an account of their use of energy. The analysis distinguishes two types of energy use: within-place and between-place fuel consumption. Thus, the effects on energy use of land use and transport policies may be assessed. At an urban or regional scale, between-places fuel consumption, by transport, is readily estimated. Within-place fuel consumption, for space heating and other purposes, must be estimated at a much finer scale in order to obtain significant results. In order to address this problem, a simulation incorporating hierarchical spatial disaggregation is described and discussed.

Introduction

The purpose of the land use and transport model described in this paper is to serve as a framework for the assessment of energy use at an urban or regional scale. Such an assessment assists the investigation of the relationship between settlement patterns, the use of land for various purposes, and the arrangement and pattern of use of the transport system. Furthermore, it is only through an integrated land use and transport model that energy use can be properly related to the benefits derived from the use of land and of transport. This is a rather important point, since otherwise the definition of which land use or transport policy is to be preferred from an energy point of view can be misguided.

The model described here simulates the interaction between two main types of activities. The first type of activity occurs in specific, fixed locations: these are residential activities, industrial production, commercial and retail services, and so on. Fuel is consumed as these activities are performed, in processes and in heating or cooling buildings. These are called 'within-place' activities, and they use 'within-place' energy. The second type of activity involves interaction between people or organizations in the form of movements of people themselves or of commodities. These movements are called 'between-places' activities, and they are users of 'between-places' energy.

In both cases the relationship between fuel consumption and user-benefit must be kept in mind. For instance, if a particular land use policy were to result, on average, in smaller homes, a substantial amount of heating fuel might be saved. However, there is no intrinsic merit in an arrangement that saves a lot of fuel simply by reducing the standard of living of the population. A successful land use policy in terms of energy use would be one which was able to maintain the same level of satisfaction with reduced fuel consumption. It must be considered also that there are economic costs to the users which are an intrinsic part of their degree of benefit. In this case land rent plays an important role, and land use policies can affect the relationship between land availability and floorspace consumption, and thus affect the cost to residents.

Similar arguments may be advanced with respect to 'between-places' activities and energy. In this case, a particular land use or transport policy cannot merely try to minimize the number of trips in order to save fuel. For example, an increase in public transport fares might reduce the number of trips that are actually made, but at the same time it would almost certainly reduce the level of benefit to trip-makers. In this example, the direct cost to users, the users' benefits, and fuel consumption are all interrelated.

Furthermore, land use and transport are also closely related: the location of activities determines the length and frequency of trips, and accessibility in turn affects land uses. A further complication is that land use and transport policies may have different effects upon different social groups, and these, in turn, may have different patterns of fuel consumption. On one hand, fuel tends to be expensive and higher income groups tend to consume more of it. On the other hand, particular policies may affect some groups more than others. For example, a fuel-saving policy such as an increase in bus fares will have a strong impact on low-income groups, but an increase in the price of petrol will hit high-income car owners harder. Contrary to what happens in a productive process, where everybody would agree that fuel-saving at a constant level of output is a desirable goal, in an urban or regional system, fuel-saving is a matter not only of efficiency, but also of distribution of resources and benefits, and therefore a matter of political choice.

This paper begins by explaining the theoretical framework on which the land use and transport model is based. This is followed by a brief description of its main operational features, including the procedures for the calculation and evaluation of fuel consumption and users' benefits.

Theoretical framework

This land use and transport model, which is called TRANUS, has been under development since 1982. Its original purpose was for the comparative evaluation of urban and regional settlement patterns from the point of view of energy use (de la Barra and Rickaby, 1982; Rickaby, 1985), but it soon became apparant that the model has more general application to the evaluation of land use and transport policies at an urban or regional scale (de la Barra, Perez and Vera, 1984). The features of the model are as follows:

- Simplicity and efficiency of operation, and in particular the capability of implementation on small microcomputers. Many more traditionally structured models are too large and complex for this, and are cumbersome when used in research. TRANUS, however, is structured in such a way that there is little need to sacrifice detail in this kind of application. Particularly with respect to the study of transport, TRANUS provides a sophisticated simulation tool.

- Theoretical consistency. In contrast with many other implemented models, TRANUS is theoretically consistent throughout, and is not a collection of sub-models of different kinds each with its own theoretical basis. The adoption of a single theoretical framework for the representation of all land use and transport phenomena is advantageous because it provides both an improved formulation and computational advantages.

- Efficiency should not only include computational aspects, but also economy of data and ease of calibration. A substantial amount of work has been devoted to these aspects, and this has enabled the model to be applied to a large number of academic and real-world studies. Spatial hierarchies have been introduced into the model in order to make savings in data collection in such studies.

A substantial amount of literature has accumulated on spatial interaction models in the areas both of land use and of transport. The first-generation gravity-type models of the 60s, and the first operational transport models were followed by the important work of

Wilson (1970, 1974), which not only introduced entropy-maximizing techniques but also led the way towards integrated land use and transport models. Wilson showed that land use and transport activities could be represented by a common theoretical framework. The work of Echenique *et al.* (1977) is also important because of the introduction of micro-economic principles and input-output analysis into modelling, and because of the high degree of implementation achieved.

TRANUS is rooted in the tradition of Wilson's and Echenique's work, but also draws heavily on the work of Domencich and McFadden (1975) on decision theory and random utility. Although these authors did propose a general model, most of their work is centred on the problem of modal choice in transportation, and no specific models are proposed for the rest of the elements of the urban structure. The theory that will be briefly described here can be considered as an extension and a generalization of their work. In the land use part of the model, TRANUS utilizes an input-output formulation as developed by Leontief and Strout (1963), and incorporates a particular way of representing it in spatial terms.

Individual and aggregated choices: the random utility approach

In general terms, decision theory describes social processes as a set of decisions made by individuals. The main assumption here is that individuals choose rationally between the options available to them. An individual, faced with a number of options, will rank them according to the degree of satisfaction or utility perceived in each case, and will then choose the one that provides the greatest utility. Utility, on the other hand, is a subjective concept - its perception will vary from one individual to another, and from one choice to another.

Mathematically, utility can be represented as a 'utility function' for a particular individual, which contains variables describing measurable characteristics of each option. Faced with a particular set of options, an individual may be assumed to evaluate each one with the same utility function, and will choose that option which yields the greatest utility.

This is the basis of micro-economic theory. However, for the urban analyst it is of little practical value, since it would be impossible to keep track of utility functions for each individual living in a city or region, and also because the number of options can be very large. There is, then, a need for aggregation. Individuals are grouped according to socio-economic characteristics and options into groups of similar type. Spatial aggregation is important: point location of individuals or organizations is replaced by location in areas called 'zones'.

Unfortunately, traditional micro-economic analysis does not provide a means of aggregating utility functions. Aggregation introduces sources of variability, because individuals within a group are different and perceive utility in different ways. The same can be said about options and spatial location. Naturally, if groups are small, variations will be small also.

In order to solve this problem, random utility theory assumes that, since we have no grounds to assume a particular distribution of the way utility is perceived within a group, all we can do is to assume that it is randomly distributed. The same will apply to options and spatial location. Utility functions will no longer apply to a particular individual: instead, they will apply to a population of individuals, and to groups of options. A population-related utility function will not only contain the aggregate measurable characteristics of each option group, but will have to contain random elements as well. Alternatively, we can assume that the utility function itself is random.

In the individual case, the utility function is deterministic, that is, it produces a unique result: the selection of an option. In the aggregate case, since there are random elements, utility functions are probabilistic, producing a distribution of results. In this case, the decision-making population are distributed probabilistically among the groups of options.

The perception of utility within the group has a particular distribution, which is the same for all option groups, i.e. there is a joint distribution. Mathematically, the probabilistic model is obtained by integrating the joint distribution. Hence, several models can be derived from the general one according to the particular shape of the distribution. Domencich and McFadden (1975) explored several shapes, particularly the Normal, Logistic and Cauchy functions; after integration, these functions yield the Probit, Logit and Arctangent models respectively. They also analysed the Weibull distribution, which is similar to the Normal distribution (and also yields a Logit model), and concluded that this should be the preferred option because of its simplicity and superior statistical properties.

If the distribution of activities is Weibull, the resulting multinomial logit model is:

$$P(k,s) = \frac{\exp\{b(s).X(k)\}}{\displaystyle\sum_{k=1}^{N}\exp\{b(s).X(k)\}} \tag{1}$$

where P(k,s) is the probability that individuals of group s choose option k; X(k) represents the measurable attributes of option k, and b(s) is a parameter that regulates the particular shape of the joint distribution of utilities perceived by group s. N is the total number of groups of options.

An interesting corollary to this, as described by Williams (1977), is that if expression (1) is the correct model, then there is one and only one way of measuring the average utility of population s:

$$S(s) = \frac{1}{b(s)}\ln[\sum_{k=1}^{N}\exp\{b(s).X(k)\}] \tag{2}$$

where S(s) is the aggregate perceived utility (or surplus) of group s.

Some properties of parameter b(s) are worth noting. If, in a particular utility function, measurable attributes X(k) represent costs, then the parameter will be negative. On the other hand, since there are several options k, one of them will represent the 'minimum cost option', say k^*. As the value of b(s) tends to minus infinity, probability $P(k^*,s)$ tends to one. However, as b(s) tends to zero, the probabilities of all options become equal, that is, P(k,s)=1/N. The value of the parameter is also related to the degree of dispersion of the distribution of utilities. If the parameter is large and negative, it indicates that all individuals within the group tend to agree on what is the best option. The parameter is also related to the level of aggregation of the groups involved: if the decision-making group is small and homogeneous, the parameter will be large and negative. In the limit, when the group is restricted to one member, the parameter will be minus infinity, and the model will be equivalent to the deterministic micro-economic model.

Decision chains and hierarchies

The paragraphs above have dealt with one particular choice situation. In an urban or regional system, however, a long and complex decision chain can be established. A typical chain would be, for example:

place of work → residence → shopping → transport mode

Each link along the chain is clearly conditioned by the preceding link. For instance, where to go shopping is a decision conditioned by the place of residence. In order to represent such a decision chain in a set of models, each component must precede the next in the right order. If each link along the chain has a corresponding mode, producing probabilities such as $P(w)$, $P(r)$, $P(s)$ and $P(m)$ in the example above, the number of people travelling by bus mode from an origin to a destination that in turn work in a particular zone could be calculated as the number of people that work in that zone x $P(r)$ x (Ps) x $P(bus)$. This is quite a comfortable solution, because it is possible to model each link of the decision chain separately, thus avoiding very large computations.

However, the problem is more complex than this, because each link in the chain may influence the preceding ones! In the above example, it could well be that people decide where to go shopping precisely because there is a good bus service. Thus the choice of transport mode affects the choice of shopping. Similarly, the choice of residential location may have been influenced by the availability of local shopping facilities.

In order to accommodate this, the process of calculation must begin from the other end, that is, from the last link in the chain, proceeding backwards. In the example, we would have to calculate the overall availability of transport from residence to shopping. Following Williams (1977), the only way to do this is by applying equation (2) and, in this case, the number of options would be the number of different modes available from the place of residence to the particular shopping centre. Equation (2) would then produce the overall aggregated utility. The model would then proceed to calculate the aggregate utility of all shopping facilities around each residential area. In this way the transport element has been transferred into the shopping utility, and eventually into the residential utility. On reaching the end of the decision chain, the model must then reverse direction and follow it again in the original direction, calculating the probabilities.

The calculation process would end here if it was not for variable costs and elasticities. In the above example, if the bus service is used beyond its capacity, the cost of travel (or time) may increase until residents eventually choose other options. This effect may be further transferred to the residential choice. Thus the calculation process becomes iterative, aggregating utilities and estimating probabilities backwards and forwards several times until a state of equilibrium is reached.

Sometimes a particular choice is divided into sub-choices, and this gives rise to the notion of hierarchy in the decision-making process. For example, residential choice might be divided into two hierarchical levels: first, the choice of a district within the city, and then the choice of a neighbourhood within a district. Similarly, a hierarchy of transport modes might be established: first, the choice of public rather than private transport, and then the choice of buses rather than other options such as trains or the subway. These hierarchical levels are related to each other in exactly the same way as different items in the decision-making chain, and the computing process is identical. Note that even if it is the same decision, the fact that it has been split into hierarchical levels means that the resulting b parameters are bound to be different.

The concept of hierarchical analysis is a powerful one. The use of hierarchies permits the representation of some parts of the urban system in great detail, while other parts of the system are dealt with in less detail. For instance, it may be of interest to investigate residential location within a particular district: in this case the residential model can determine the probable location of residences in all districts at a first hierarchical level, and only apply a second level to the district in question. It is important, however, that these levels of analysis should not be confused.

The algorithmic and operational structure of the model

In this section, the sequence of calculations and the computer program that make up the land use and transport model are briefly described.

The dynamic structure of the model

The two main components of the model are a land use model and a transport model, and these components have an explicit way of interacting through time, as shown in Figure 1. It can be seen from the figure that simulations of the behaviour of the urban system are made for a sequence of time periods, denoted as t1, t2,... The land use model first simulates time period t1, and calculates the demand for transport in that period t1. Between period t1 and t2 there might be a growth or decay in the total number of activities, or changes in land use policies. To take account of such changes, the land use model next simulates time period t2, and the modified transport demand is fed into the transport model, which simulates the same period. This process is repeated for all time periods. However, the simulation made by the transport model includes the calculation of accessibilities, and when known these affect the location of activities. In reality, this feedback from transport to land uses does not occur instantly, because land uses take some time to respond. To account for this time-lag, the accessibilities produced by the transport model for a given time period are used by the land use model for the following time period. Similarly, output obtained from the land use model for a given period can affect the simulations made for the next time period.

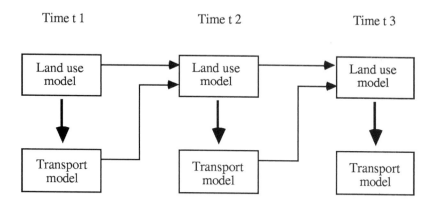

Figure 1   *The dynamic structure of the model*

The calculation sequence of the land use and transport model

Figure 2 shows the main steps in the sequence of calculation. Each step will now be described in turn.

1) *Global input-output model.* The first step in the sequence is a global input output model which simulates the overall level of activities within the study area. The model is a traditional input-output model with an iterative solution: it distinguishes between final demand sectors of employment. A number of induced activities (service employment and residences) are calculated from the location of basic employment through a set of intersectoral coefficients. A variable number of basic and induced sectors may be specified, and each sector may accommodate either positive or negative growth from one time period to the next.

2) *Location of basic activities.* If between time periods there has been an increment in basic activities, then such increments are allocated to zones and added to previous values. Growth is simply distributed according to user-defined weighted attractor variables, though the user may also specify particular allocations exogenously. If the increment is negative, the model automatically reverses the weighting.

3) *Location of the supply of floorspace.* If there has been a positive increment in activities, the model calculates how much extra floorspace is required. The new floorspace is then added to the total floorspace in each zone, taking into account both exogenously-specified land use regulations and land-rent values obtained for the previous time period. The user may specify particular zonal quantities of floorspace exogenously. If there has been a negative increment in activities, the floorspace calculated for the previous time period is left unchanged.

4) *Location of induced activities.* Whether or not the total number of activities has changed, the model calculates all spatial interactions between induced activities and determines their locations. This is achieved by a spatial input-output mode, from which a set of matrices of 'functional flows' is obtained. These flows will eventually become the demand for transportation. Spatial distributions are made by multinomial logit models, in which the utility functions are based on generalized transport costs and land rents. Distributions are also affected by user-defined weighted attractor variables. In all allocation procedures, whether of basic or induced activities or of floorspace, a two-level hierarchy of zones can be specified.

5) *Calculation of the demand for floorspace.* Once all activities have been allocated to zones, the model applies floorspace demand functions, in which the demand for floorspace is a function of land rent and of given elasticities. Total floorspace demand in each zone is simply the sum of the amounts of floorspace demanded by each activity in that zone.

6) *Adjustment of land rents.* For each zone the demand for floorspace is compared with the available supply calculated at step 3. If the demand and supply values are different, then land-rent values are adjusted upwards or downwards accordingly. The calculation sequence then returns to stage 4 and revised locations of induced activities are obtained. This iterative process continues until demand is equal to supply in all zones, within specified convergency critieria.

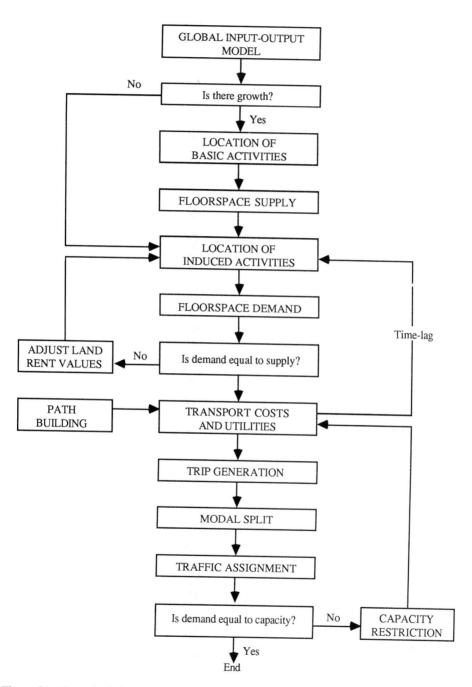

Figure 2   *The calculation sequence for the land use and transport model*

7) *Path-building through a transport network.* The transportation network of the area under study is represented as a set of connected links. Each link is assigned a number of characteristics: link type, link length, traffic capacity (for each mode), and turn prohibitions. Each mode in turn can include a variable number of operators, typically bus routes, mass transit, cargo operators, and so on. The purpose of the path-building algorithm is to define, for each origin and destination zone and for each mode, the first n paths, n being a user-defined number. The first path will always be the one which provides the shortest journey time, and the n paths will be ordered by journey time. The user may also define a 'dispersion factor', representing how much longer than the minimum path any other path is permitted to be. If, in a given mode, there is more than one operator, paths may contain transfers from one operator to another, and such transfers will involve waiting times calculated by the model as a function of the user-defined frequency of each operator. The algorithm to do this is based on Dijkstra's (1959) original method for finding the shortest path through a network; in order to find several paths instead of just the minimum, this algorithm has been made n-dimensional and elaborated to allow it to keep track of operators and inter-operator transfers. Turn prohibitions are dealt with by a unique method whereby the externally specified representation of the network is transformed into an internal reverse graph in which road sections are represented by vertices and junctions by links.

8) *Transport costs and utilities.* Once the set of paths has been determined, it is necessary to estimate the cost of travelling along each path. This must include not only out-of-pocket expenses (i.e. fares, fuel costs) but also the value of time to the individual making the trip. The value of time is found to vary according to the income level of the traveller and the purpose of the trip (for example, trips to work are valued more highly than shopping trips). Transfer costs and times are included in these calculations. Trips are divided into 'transport categories' according to the income levels of the travellers and the purposes of the trips. Once travel costs have been determined for every path, transport category and mode, they are aggregated across all paths and all modes by successive applications of equation (2).

9) *Trip generation.* At this step the number of trips is calculated from the corresponding land use flows previously determined at step 4. The number of trips is calculated according to an elastic model, and varies with the generalized cost of travel as calculated at step 8. Different elasticities may be applied to each transport category.

10) *Modal split.* All trips are assigned to modes by means of a multinomial logit model and according to the transport costs calculated at step 8 and the availability of transport for each transport category. 'Commodity categories' are assigned to goods modes and 'person-categories' are assigned to passenger modes. Car ownership limitations are applied in the latter cases.

11) *Traffic assignment.* At this step all trips by each category and mode are assigned by a multinomial logit model to the paths that were determined at step 7. Travel costs at a path level, as determined at step 8, become utility functions. All trips along each link in the transport network are transformed into 'standard vehicles' (according to specified occupancy rates for various vehicles such as cars, buses and trains), and are then added together at a link level in order to obtain travel demand by mode in each section of the transport network.

12)   *Capacity restriction.* Here, travel demand at link level is compared with link capacities in order to determine the reduction of free-flow traffic speed as a function of congestion. Each mode may have a different initial free-flow speed, and speed is reduced according to different parameters of a common capacity-restriction function. Where a travel mode includes more than one operator (as in the case of some public transport mode trips), waiting times are increased at transfer points. Ratios of demand to capacity are calculated for each operator in every link. Once the travel speeds and waiting times have been adjusted, the calculation procedure returns to step 8 and transport costs, which are affected by the increased travel times, are recalculated. Steps 8 to 12 are repeated until specified convergency criteria are met.

The evaluation procedure

The purpose of the evaluation procedure is to assess the effect on an urban area or region of various changes which might be made to the pattern of land uses: the thermal characteristics of buildings, the pattern of travel, the characteristics of the transport system, or the cost of fuel (or indeed of policies designed to result in such changes). The assessment is made by comparing the system in an initial state (the 'base case') with one or more modified versions of the same system (the 'options'). Separate runs of the land use and transport model are made for the base case and for each of the options, and results are stored in output files. The evaluation procedure is contained in a program which reads the output from the land use and transport model and presents tables of data to indicate the performance of the options under study. These data include the size and location of residential populations, the amounts and locations of employment and services, the location and cost of floorspace, the numbers of trips by each mode, and their average lengths, durations and costs, and the overall operational and overhead costs of the transport system.

However, the main focus of the evaluation is on within-place and between-places fuel consumption, and on the overall value, or benefit to the population, of living and working in the environment of the option under study (relative to the other options). The 'user-benefit' is derived from the utility functions at the heart of the land use and transport model, and takes into account the overall aggregated availability and cost of accommodation and travel, including the cost of transport fuel and the effects of congestion. In comparing the user-benefits to be derived from the base case with the user-benefits to be derived from a particular option, the model applies the following equation adapted from Cochrane (1975):

$$DS(s) = \frac{1}{b(s)} \ln \left[\frac{\sum_{k=1}^{N} \exp\{b(s).X(k)\} \, [1]}{\sum_{k=1}^{N} \exp\{b(s).X(k)\} \, [0]} \right] \qquad (3)$$

where DS(s) is the difference in overall utility or user-benefit between the base case [0] and the option [1] with which it is being compared. The value of DS(s) is positive if the population is better off than in the base case, and negative if it is not.

In a dynamic evaluation, all costs and benefits to the population are calculated on an annual basis and discounted at a specified rate. The resulting net present values of modifications to the base case are used in conjunction with capital costs in the calculation of internal and discounted rates of return for each time period of the model. It is not intended that these economic indicators are used to establish a preference for a particular option, rather that the comprehensive set of evaluation tables, embracing statistical data, costs and user-benefits, provides a basis for the assessment of the options under consideration.

The calculation of fuel consumption

The calculation of within-place fuel consumption

The model calculates the fuel demand, for space-heating purposes, of dwellings within the area under study. The authors intend to extend the model, in due course, to incorporate the calculation of space-heating fuel demand for a range of non-domestic building types. For dwellings, the model uses data on the characteristics of the housing stock in the area under study, and relates fuel demand for space-heating to the size of the dwelling (i.e. the amount of floorspace it contains). The land use model makes a distribution of households into dwellings located in each of the zones into which the study area is divided. The size of these dwellings varies between externally specified limits in accordance with the cost of land (which itself is determined by availability and demand). It is therefore necessary to specify the relationship between the size of dwellings and their fuel demand for the region under study. This relationship depends upon the climate, the characteristics of the buildings, and the pattern of occupancy and use, and it will therefore vary with the location of the area under study.

As an example, the following paragraphs report the procedure used in the specification of the appropriate relationship for the British housing stock, on a time horizon twenty-five years in the future, and for a range of three energy scenarios describing possible future conditions of fuel availability. The scenarios are: 'business as usual', a scenario of high economic growth in which fuel conservation is not a priority; 'technical fix', a scenario of high economic growth in which fuel conservation is achieved by means of technical improvements to buildings and vehicles; and 'very low energy', a scenario of low economic growth and intense fuel conservation through both technical improvements and changes in lifestyle. The scenarios are described in detail elsewhere (Rickaby, 1985).

Penz (1983) presents data on over 400 randomly-chosen Cambridge dwellings, including total internal floor area and useful heat demand for space-heating over the heating season. A simple linear regression of these two variables for 375 of the sampled houses, using the Numerical Algorithms Group mark 11 Fortran routine G02CAF, yields the relationship:

$$UE = 114.26 \, A + 2390.46 \tag{4}$$

where UE is the average useful energy demand per dwelling over the heating season (in kWh), and A is the floorspace area of the dwelling (in square metres). Hence we have:

$$DE = \frac{UEn}{f} \tag{5}$$

$$DE = \frac{(114.26 \, Az + 2390.46)n}{f} \tag{6}$$

where in a given zone DE is the total fuel demand of the dwellings in that zone, over the heating season (kWh delivered energy); f represents the overall conversion efficiency of the heating systems in all the dwellings in that zone ($0 < f < 1$); Az is the average area of the dwellings in that zone; and n represents the number of dwellings in that zone. It is therefore necessary to establish a value for the overall conversion efficiency, f. Leach and Pellew (1982) suggest that for British housing in 1980, f=0.67. However, the conversion efficiency varies from house to house according to the type of fuel used, and whether the house has central heating or not. Leach and Pellew (1982) present data on this subject for British housing in 1980, as in Table 1.

Type of dwelling	Proportion of stock	Conversion efficiency
Without central heating	0.418	-
With central heating (gas, oil or solid fuel)	0.477	0.65
With central heating (electric)	0.105	0.95
Overall	1.000	0.67

Table 1   *Conversion efficiencies for the British housing stock, by heating type, 1980 (source: Leach and Pellew, 1982)*

From this data a value of 0.64 can be derived for the conversion efficiency of non centrally-heated houses.

The above data is for 1980, but the TRANUS model is required in this example to simulate conditions at the scenario horizon, twenty-five years in the future, i.e. in 2010. Leach and Pellew point out that the proportion of British houses with central heating has been growing at about 3% per year since 1964, that there is no sign of this growth slowing down, and that centrally-heated houses are generally kept warmer than non centrally-heated houses to the extent that their useful fuel demand is about 30% to 35% higher. In recent years the growth in central heating has been balanced by increased levels of insulation, so that overall fuel demand has been roughly constant (Leach and Pellew, 1982).

Because of saturation effects, ownership of central heating is unlikely to continue to grow at 3% per year. Assume therefore that in 2010 there is a 90% ownership of central heating, and that the individual efficiencies and the proportion of electric to gas, oil and solid fuel central heating are constant, then the properties of the housing stock in 2010 will be as in Table 2.

Type of dwelling	Proportion of stock	Conversion efficiency
Without central heating	0.100	0.64
With central heating (gas, oil or solid fuel)	0.740	0.65
With central heating (electric)	0.160	0.95
Overall	1.000	0.68

Table 2 *Projected conversion efficiencies for the British housing stock, by heating type, 2010*

Now consider the balance between improved heating standards and levels of insulation. The prevailing situation in Britain, in which improved standards are roughly balanced by increased insulation is similar to the 'technical fix' scenario in which technical improvements are made without any reduction in standards of living or expectations. The model must however be able to simulate the effects of different approaches, embodied in other scenarios, and in particular the 'business-as-usual' scenario and the 'very low energy' scenarios which characterize a range of different possibilities.

In the 'business-as-usual' scenario, living standards continue to improve in line with trends in the early 1970s, without compensating technical improvements. This scenario must therefore include the increased penetration of central heating, and consequent improved overall conversion efficiency and adoption of higher internal temperatures.

Similarly, in the 'very low energy' scenario, intensive fuel conservation through technical improvements is combined with reduced living standards. In domestic space heating this scenario would involve a halt to the introduction of central heating, and the maximum realistic penetration of solar heating.

Both of these effects, and the balance of improved standards and increased insulation in the middle 'technical fix' scenario can be represented by a 'retrofit factor', introduced into equation 6:

$$DE = \frac{(114.26\ Az + 2390.46)nR}{f} \qquad (7)$$

where R is the retrofit factor, for which different values must be determined for each scenario.

Leach and Pellew (1982) suggest that for every 10% increase in ownership of central heating (relative to the whole stock) there is a 1.3% increase in overall useful energy demand. Assuming that in the 'business-as-usual' scenario 90% of dwellings are centrally-heated, there would have been 32% growth in central heating since 1980, and therefore a 4.2% increase in useful energy demand. This suggests a value for R of 1.042.

In the 'technical fix' scenario the same growth in ownership of central heating and in useful energy demand is compensated for by increased insulation. Therefore the value to be assumed for R is 1.

In the 'very low energy' scenario, there is no increase in central heating ownership or in useful energy demand for space heating. Instead there is increased insulation coupled with the introduction of supplementary solar heating. Penz (1983) has suggested that the solar heating technologies most appropriate to the British housing stock are the conservatory, the roofspace collector, and the Trombe wall, applied in that order of priority, in conjunction with increased insulation, and primarily to solid-walled dwellings wherever possible. Penz has simulated the effects of this scenario as applied to the sample of 413 Cambridge houses, and estimated the effect of its application to the whole of Britain's housing as a reduction of overall energy demand for space heating to 69% of the 1980 level. This suggests that an appropriate value for R in the low scenario is 0.69.

In summary, therefore, the fuel demand for domestic space heating may be calculated as follows:

$$DE = \frac{0.0036(114.26\ Az + 2390.46)nR}{f} \qquad (8)$$

where in a given zone DE is the total fuel demand of the dwellings in that zone, over the heating season (GJ delivered energy); Az is the average floor area of the dwellings in that zone (m); f represents the overall conversion efficiency of heating systems in all the dwellings in that zone (0<f<1), exogenously specified, according to the scenario; n is the number of dwellings in that zone; R is the 'retrofit parameter', exogenously specified, according to the scenario; and the factor 0.0036 converts kilowatt-hours to gigajoules.

For the British housing stock, and for three scenarios in this example, the appropriate parameters are as in Table 3.

Scenario	BAU	TF	VLE
Overall conversion efficiency, f	0.680	0.680	0.670
Retrofit parameter, R	1.046	1.000	0.690

Table 3 *Projected overall conversion efficiencies and retrofit parameters, by scenarios, for the British housing stock in 2010*

Then to aggregate demand over N zones in the model, we have:

$$Ewp = \sum_{i=1}^{i=N} DE \qquad (9)$$

where Ewp is the annual within-place fuel demand for space-heating of the housing stock, in all zones, in gigajoules.

The calculation of between-places fuel consumption

The fuel consumption of transport vehicles is a subject which has been very thoroughly studied during the past decade, and there exists a wealth of research about present-day vehicles and much speculation about future vehicles. Typically both road and rail vehicles are used for urban and regional passenger transport.

The model calculates the annual fuel demand for passenger transport within the area under study. All specified modes of public transport are taken into account, according to externally specified data for each mode. Goods transport is not included in the calculations, but since it can be readily incorporated in the trip generation algorithm of the transport model, the authors intend to extend the application of the model, in due course, to incorporate the fuel demand of delivery vehicles and intra-urban goods transport.

As has already been described, the transport model calculates the daily total number of passenger trips made by the population of the area under study. Trips for different purposes are simulated separately: trips between homes and places of work, and trips between homes and services are distinguished by different levels of benefit to the consumer making the trip. This differentiates, in the simulation, between relatively frequent trips, for example to buy groceries, and less frequent, less essential trips, for example to department stores or to places of entertainment. The model assigns all these trips to modes (public or private vehicles) and to routes through the network which represents the pattern of major and minor roads. For each trip, the length of the journey and the average speed are calculated link by link. In order to calculate the fuel consumption of the city-region's vehicles, it is necessary to combine this information with data on the fuel consumption of vehicles in relation to their speed. As an example, the following paragraphs describe the procedure used in the specification of the relationship between fuel consumption and speed for two assumed British private cars, on a twenty-five year time horizon, and in the context of the same three scenarios referred to above (Rickaby, 1985).

Table 4 presents data for two contemporary private cars, the Ford Granada 2000GL MK2 (1983), and the Vauxhall Cavalier 1300SL (1983). This data was obtained by plotting and interpolating the manufacturers' official figures, which are displayed on vehicles in showrooms and widely published in motoring journals.

The Ford Granada has been adopted in this example as a representative larger car which might be considered a typical car in the 'business-as-usual' scenario. In that scenario the average fuel consumption of cars is expected to increase, relative to the present day. The Vauxhall Cavalier is a typical medium-sized car today, and the 1300SL is one of the more fuel-efficient models in the range. This vehicle is adopted for the 'technical fix' scenario and the 'very low energy' scenario, in both of which the fuel consumption of average present-day cars is assumed to be reduced by half. The fuel consumption data for the Vauxhall Cavalier has therefore been transformed so that the consumption is halved at the most efficient speed, without the shape of the fuel consumption curve being altered. The resulting relationships between speed and fuel consumption are incorporated in the model as fitted curves of the form

$$F = c + \lambda\, e^{\delta V} \tag{10}$$

Speed (km/hr)	Fuel consumption (l/km)	
	Granada	Cavalier
10	0.151	0.114
20	0.132	0.100
30	0.117	0.089
40	0.103	0.079
50	0.092	0.072
60	0.084	0.068
70	0.079	0.062
80	0.076	0.061
90	0.077	0.064
100	0.082	0.070
110	0.090	0.079
120	0.101	0.088
130	0.120	0.100

Table 4   *Fuel consumption data for typical British cars: Granada = Ford Granada 2000GL MK2, 1983 model; Cavalier = Vauxhall Cavalier 1300SL, 1983 model (source: manufacturers' published figures, plotted and intermediate values interpolated)*

where F is the fuel consumption per unit distance travelled, and V is the vehicle's average speed (measured over one link of the transport network), c is a constant, and λ and δ are parameters. Table 5 shows the values of c, λ and δ, and for the fitted curves; these parameter values give good correspondence between calculated and plotted values of F for the assumed range of average speeds in the transport model (from 5 to 80 km/hr).

Public transport buses and minibuses can be treated in a similar way, and equivalent procedures are adopted to obtain fuel consumption curves for other modes of transport. By means of these procedures the transport model is able to calculate the daily consumption of fuel by all modes of transport in the study area. Volumetric quantities of petrol (for cars) and diesel fuel (for buses), plus electric power (for railways) are then converted into gigajoules. Petrol is assumed to provide 34.945 MJ/litre and diesel fuel is assumed to provide 38.242 MJ/litre. Annual between-places energy use may then be estimated from:

Scenario	BAU	TF	VLE
c	0.065	0.025	0.025
λ	0.110	0.083	0.083
δ	-0.025	-0.025	-0.025

Table 5   *Projected fuel consumption parameters for private cars, for curves of the form $F = c + \lambda e^{\delta V}$, where F is the fuel consumption of the vehicle (l/km) and V is the vehicle's speed*

$$E_{bp} = 300\ (f_p + f_d + f_e) \tag{11}$$

where E_{bp} is the annual (between-places) energy use for transport, f_p is weekday energy use in petrol-powered private cars, f_d is weekday energy use in diesel-powered public service buses, and f_e is the weekday energy use in electric vehicles. Other fuels can be incorporated in the same way. The factor 300 is a convention adopted to represent 261 annual working weekdays and 39 additional working days which are assumed equivalent to 52 weekends.

Conclusion

The model described above has been successfully implemented on a wide range of machines, including both microcomputers and larger minicomputers, and has been used in a number of theoretical and practical studies. The particular procedures described here for the calculation of fuel consumption have been included in the model implemented in Fortran 77 on a Digital Equipment Corporation VAX 11/780 machine at The Open University, and which is being used in energy studies of British urban and regional settlement patterns (Rickaby, 1985).

Successful implementation of the model for the purpose of energy analysis depends on the availability of data from which the characteristics of the stock of transport vehicles and of houses (and eventually other buildings) in the study area can be deduced. Data on vehicles, and on the British housing stock, are readily available, but more research is required in order to extend the model to include building types or for application to other study areas. The authors are currently investigating the energy-related characteristics of buildings and groups of buildings in British provincial towns and cities. This will permit the extension of the TRANUS model, in due course, to include assessment of space heating demands for commercial accommodation in central urban areas.

The TRANUS model is intended for use in systematic studies of urban and regional land use and transport patterns. However, use of the model for energy analysis at an urban or regional scale underlines the importance of similar studies focused on individual buildings, building types, groups of buildings and building stocks. Such studies indicate possibilities and opportunities for development within the overall constraints which may be identified by simulation at the urban or regional scale. Conversely, the analysis at the urban and regional scale relies on an understanding of the energy-related characteristics of built form at a local and intermediate scale, and of local stocks of buildings such as houses, offices, schools and factories. Energy analysis in urban and regional modelling, by means of models such as TRANUS, must therefore proceed in parallel with studies of energy use in individual buildings, and in relation to urban built form.

References

Cochrane, F.A. (1975). A possible economic base for the gravity model. *Journal of Transport Economics and Policy*, Vol. 9, No. 1, pp. 34-49.

de la Barra, T., Perez, B. and Vera, N. (1984). TRANUS-J: putting large models into small computers. *Environment and Planning B: Planning and Design*, Vol. 11, pp. 87-101.

de la Barra, T. and Rickaby, P.A. (1982). Modelling regional energy use: a land-use, transport and energy-evaluation model. *Environment and Planning B*, Vol. 9, pp. 429-443.

Dijkstra, E.W. (1959). A note on two problems in connexion with graphs. *Numerische Mathematik*, Vol. 1, pp. 269-271.

Domencich, T.A. and McFadden, D. (1975). *Urban Travel Demand: a Behavioural Analysis*. Amsterdam: North Holland.

Echenique, M. *et al.* (1977). *Teheran Development Council Secretariat Land Use Transport Model Pilot Study: Final Report*. Cambridge: Applied Research of Cambridge Ltd.

Leach, G. and Pellew S. (1982). *Energy Conservation in Housing*. London: International Institute for the Environment and Development.

Leontief, W.W. and Stout, A. (1963). Multi-regional input-output analysis. In T. Barna (ed.), *Structural Interdependence and Economic Development*. London: Macmillan.

Penz, F. (1983). *Passive Solar Heating in Existing Dwellings: a Study of Potential in the Existing Housing Stock of the United Kingdom*. Report to the Energy Technology Support Unit, Harwell. Cambridge: The Martin Centre for Architectural and Urban Studies.

Rickaby, P.A. (1985). *Towards a Spatial Energy Model: a Theoretical Comparison of Accessibility and Energy-Use in Regional Settlement Patterns*. Research Project Report, Centre for Configurational Studies, The Open University, Milton Keynes.

Williams, H.C.W.L. (1977). On the formation of travel demand models and economic evaluation of user-benefit. *Environment and Planning A*, Vol. 9, pp. 285-344.

Wilson, A. (1970). *Entropy in Urban and Regional Modelling*. Monographs in Spatial and Environmental System Analysis. London: Pion.

Wilson, A. (1974). *Urban and Regional Models in Geography and Planning*. London: Wiley.

A METHOD FOR DETERMINING ENERGY FLOWS IN URBAN BUILT FORM

Leslie Matthews

Architectural Directorate
Ministry of Works and Development, New Zealand

Abstract

A failing in many urban energy models lies in their inability to account for space heating and other energy demands within entire urban building sectors. The problem is exacerbated by the wide range of possible urban building types and associated spatial configurations which, in turn, influence internal energy demand and external solar accessibility. This paper reports on a simple, computer-based method for determining energy flows within contiguous buildings at the urban block scale. The method embodies a survey and data input technique, statistical processing and analysis of energy-related characteristics, and three-dimensional thermal network analysis of both existing and hypothetical building characteristics. Both tubular and pictorial output assist in the interpretation of results, which are demonstrated through an application to a block of mixed-use urban buildings in Cambridge, England.

Introduction

Energy is purchased for consumption by processes which are either external to buildings or contained within buildings. Processes which belong to the latter category involve conversion of energy into forms such as heat, light and mechanical power, and their consumption may considerably outweigh that of the former category (Figure 1). In highly urbanized societies, especially, the majority of energy consumption occurs within urban built form, yet surprisingly little is known about the ways in which design professionals may advantageously influence building configurations in this regard.

The two related fields of research - urban studies and architectural science - have traditionally focused their attention away from small groupings of urban buildings. While much research has been conducted into methods of energy analysis and conservation in isolated buildings (especially dwellings), few studies have investigated contiguous groups of buildings to a similar level of detail. Urban research, on the other hand, has tended to address entire urban systems, analysing building-related energy consumption through

29

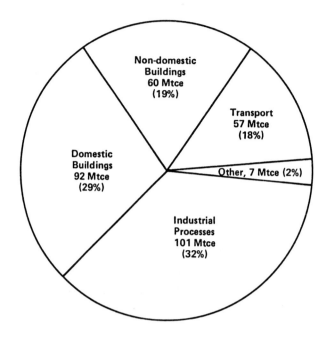

Figure 1   *In the U.K., energy consumption by processes within buildings considerably outweighs that of processes which are external to buildings (source: Gardner, 1984)*

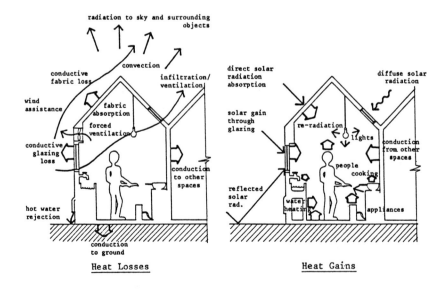

Figure 2   *Thermal influences operating on spaces within buildings*

limited and generalized parameters. Detailed analysis of groups of urban buildings remains relatively unstudied.

Reasons for a lack of analysis at the intermediate scale have to do with the complexity of the issues involved. The range of possible urban building types, uses and spatial relationships are impossible to represent by a statistical replicate, and therefore demand specific analysis. Detailed thermal network analysis of large numbers of contiguous buildings is, however, beyond the data handling capabilities of conventional building thermal models.

This paper reports on a simple, computer-based method for modelling energy consumption within contiguous groups of buildings. The method has been tested elsewhere against monitored data and has been found particularly suited to analysis of buildings at the urban block scale (Matthews, 1985). The economy of calculation, together with consideration of spatial data, enable the model to handle large amounts of data relating to complex built form configurations. The following sections of this paper address the way in which such data are input, analysed and interpreted.

Data collection and input

Data are required for the calculation of energy flows - especially thermal losses and gains - within built form. Heat is lost from buildings by convective, conductive, and radiative processes through the building fabric and through ventilation. Sources of heat gain to buildings include artificial lighting, people, appliances, and solar radiation (Figure 2). Although the parameters required for quantifying heat gains and losses in any building sample are manifold, they may largely be grouped into either physical or occupational characteristics (Figure 3).

Physical characteristics of buildings are mostly obtainable through a visual site survey while occupational aspects may be derived from questionnaires. Both types of information may, however, be collected on the same visit, and recorded on a single data record form. For this purpose a form was devised with formatting and coding which enables direct transference of data to the computer based data store (Figure 4). In this case all rooms, premises, and buildings within the sample are given a unique space identifier and their data are recorded on a hierarchical series of 80-column record cards.

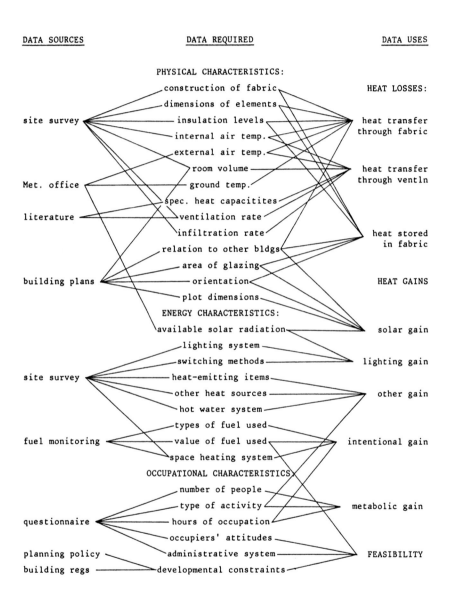

Figure 3   *Data requirements, their sources and their uses*

COL	CARD TYPE 1		CARD TYPE 2		CARD TYPE 3	
01	BUILDING	|_	ZONE	|_	ROOM	|_
02	address	|_	number	|_	floor level	|_
03	" " " "	|_	" " " "	|_	room number	|_
04	street	|_	predominant	|_	" " " "	|_
05	code	|_	use type	|_	grid code	|_
06	year built	|_	links	|_	" " " "	|_
07	" " " "	|_	total zone	|_	" " " "	|_
08	" " " "	|_	floor area	|_	" " " "	|_
09	" " " "	|_	" " " "	|_	floor area	|_
10	gross floor	|_	" " " "	|_	" " " "	|_
11	area	|_	" " " "	|_	" " " "	|_
12	" " " "	|_		|_	" " " "	|_
13	" " " "	|_	heating type	|_		|_
14	" " " "	|_	" " " "	|_	activity	|_
15	plot	|_	thermostat	|_	" " " "	|_
16	frontage	|_	setting	|_	no. people	|_
17	plot depth	|_	hot water	|_	" " " "	|_
18	" " " "	|_	lagging	|_	" " " "	|_
19		|_		|_	" " " "	|_
20	wall types	|_	ventilation	|_	occupation	|_
21	" " " "	|_	infiltration	|_	type	|_
22	wall	|_		|_	ann. breaks	|_
23	thickness	|_	electricity	|_		|_
24	" " " "	|_	1st qtr.	|_		|_
25	insulation	|_	" " " "	|_		|_
26	door types	|_	" " " "	|_	lighting	|_
27	draught-	|_	" " " "	|_	" " " "	|_
28	proofing	|_	electricity	|_	" " " "	|_
29	glass type	|_	2nd qtr.	|_	" " " "	|_
30	frame type	|_	" " " "	|_	" " " "	|_
31	weather-	|_	" " " "	|_	switching	|_
32	stripping	|_	" " " "	|_	method	|_
33		|_	electricity	|_	task lights	|_
34	roof surface	|_	3rd qtr.	|_	operation	|_
35	roof type	|_	" " " "	|_		|_
36	insulation	|_	" " " "	|_		|_
37	sth-facing	|_	" " " "	|_		|_
38	roof area	|_	electricity	|_		|_
39	" " " "	|_	4th qtr.	|_		|_
40	skylights	|_	" " " "	|_		|_

Figure 4 *Part of the form used to record survey data before transference to the computer-based data store.*

Site surveying also assists in confirming building plans which, in turn, facilitate analysis of spatial relationships. Plans constitute a record of two-dimensional data for each building level, which may be utilized when included in the data store. This task is achieved by means of a digitizing peripheral to locate boundary elements to spaces on the Cartesian plane. Each space so defined is then addressed to its associated space identifier, thereby linking the graphical data with the survey data files.

When all plan spaces are defined in this manner, net floor areas are established using linear geometrical routines. Immediate neighbours to each space may also be defined by iterative searching for Cartesian co-ordinates pertaining to other space identifiers within a proximate search area. Information pertaining to floor areas, neighbouring spaces and shared boundary lengths is then saved and included in the main data store.

Next, adjacent spaces in the third dimension are identified by vertically extruding two-dimensional descriptions in order to establish common or overlapping points. Once the vertically adjoining space identifiers are also included in the main data store, a three-dimensional network is established.

Spatial data are then available, together with all other associated data in the store, for use in the thermal analysis.

Thermal analysis

Initial analyses of collected data involve data checking and statistical processing in order to discern trends and to gain a general knowledge about the building sample. The statistical routines employed for this purpose form part of the well-documented *Statistical Package for the Social Sciences* (Nie *et al.*, 1985), which facilitates substantial data handling flexibility. Once the variables are defined, they may be significantly transformed before or during statistical processing. It is at this transformation stage that thermal calculations are performed, thereby enabling results to be grouped and statistically interpreted (Figure 5).

The requirement for economy of thermal calculations in large building samples dictates that calculations be based on steady-state theory rather than dynamic simulation, and the BRE method was selected because of its proven suitability for predicting seasonal heat balances with an acceptable degree of accuracy (Uglow, 1981). However, the method first

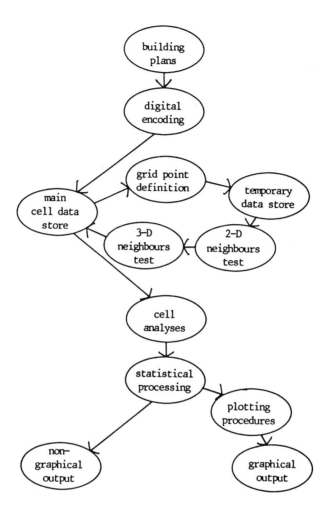

Figure 5   *Analysis of building spaces or cells occurs after elaboration of spatial data and*
before statistical processing

required extension to account for parameters relating to non-domestic buildings and a
variety of construction types. Perhaps the most influential of these parameters is mean
daily internal air temperature, which requires interpolation from monitored temperatures
during occupied periods. Monitored temperatures are then modified by the rate of thermal
decay during unoccupied periods which, in turn, is influenced by the insulation standard
and thermal capacitance of the surrounding structure.

Of course, a proportion of the internal heat gain is due to solar gain. According to the BRE method, the mean daily unobstructed solar contribution to space heating may be deduced for a given location, orientation, heating regime and elemental construction. The effect of overshadowing from surrounding obstructions is more problematic, although this may be approximated by correlating the reduction in local unobstructed seasonal solar irradiance with configuration factors. Because spatial data are available in this case, configuration factors of obstructions in relation to receiving surfaces may simply be found by iterative searching for the extent of surrounding built form located on or above the same plane as the space under analysis. For this reason it is useful to include a record of surrounding street facades and nearby tall buildings when spatial data are input.

Resultant mean daily internal air temperatures from all heat gains and losses are then used to calculate temperature differentials between the space under analysis and all adjoining spaces, the ground, and the external environment. Local daily ground and external air temperatures are derived from meteorological records, and averaged over the heating season. The seasonal heat balance equation employed in the thermal analysis is given in Figure 6.

Application

In order to test the validity and applicability of the analysis method, a case study block of thirty buildings in the central urban area of Cambridge was analysed. A set of drawings (Figure 7) of the buildings was completed and a comprehensive site survey was conducted. The survey and input stages took approximately nine working days for one person to complete.

Initial analyses of the data revealed that within the sample buildings were accommodated 51 distinct premises, 90% of which belong to either retail, catering, office, or residential categories. A corresponding variety of occupational regimes occurred, but a homogeneity of premises was found in their spatial location within buildings. Basements were mostly associated with storage facilities, ground floors with retail, first and second floors with offices and catering, and upper floors with residential uses. Wall and roof insulation were uncommon throughout the sample, and space heating system controls were found to be minimal, regardless of space activity types.

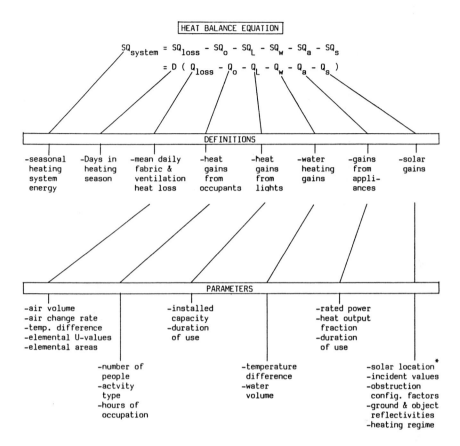

HEAT BALANCE EQUATION

$$SQ_{system} = SQ_{loss} - SQ_o - SQ_L - SQ_w - SQ_a - SQ_s$$

$$= D \, (\, Q_{loss} - Q_o - Q_L - Q_w - Q_a - Q_s \,)$$

DEFINITIONS

| -seasonal heating system energy | -Days in heating season | -mean daily fabric & ventilation heat loss | -heat gains from occupants | -heat gains from lights | -water heating gains | -gains from appli- ances | -solar gains |

PARAMETERS

-air volume
-air change rate
-temp. difference
-elemental U-values
-elemental areas

-installed
capacity
-duration
of use

-rated power
-heat output
fraction
-duration
of use

-number of
people
-actvity
type
-hours of
occupation

-temperature
difference
-water
volume

-solar location[*]
-incident values
-obstruction
config. factors
-ground & object
reflectivities
-heating regime

* solar location refers to solar altitude and azimuth in relation to irradiated surfaces

Figure 6   *The seasonal heat balance equation employed in the thermal analysis*

Thermal analyses were performed to determine both maximum hourly heat loses and mean seasonal heat balances. Results showed that maximum heat losses for the sample buildings, when normalized by floor areas and temperature differentials, bore a close correspondence to UK domestic figures (Figure 8). It was suggested that the main difference in the two sets of figures was due to inferior insulation standards (especially pertaining to walls) in the sample. Regression analysis of contributory factors highlighted exposed envelope areas, wall and floor areas, and vertical location within the built form as being particularly

Figure 7   *Ground floor plan of the case study buildings analysed*

Predicted mean seasonal heat loss components were very similar in order of influence to those of maximum heat losses, but the inclusion of heat gains introduced considerable complexities into seasonal heat balance trends. While most heat gains derived from casual sources, their distribution varied substantially according to room activity types. Gains from artificial lighting were most prominent in retail, entertainment, and office premises. Solar gains mostly affected elevated residential uses, while gains from occupants were significant only in entertainment rooms. The most concentrated gains, however, accrued from appliances in catering kitchens and machinery rooms, even allowing for forced air extraction from these spaces. Major casual gain locations were also referenced in the

BNUM	HEATLOSS	VENTρ	GLAZρ	ROOFρ	EXWALLρ	FLOORρ	BLDGS
B23B	6.5007	.1395	.1430	.3458	.2366	.0872	.0479
B12K	4.1519	.2090	.1896	.1210	.3101	.0755	.0948
B11K	4.9835	.2015	.1645	.1334	.3196	.0542	.1269
B11E	5.8949	.1675	.1676	.1122	.4230	.0661	.0636
B10K	5.7105	.2785	.1054	.0691	.2666	.0932	.1871
B09K	4.2040	.2343	.0999	.1805	.2503	.1132	.1217
B09E	7.5525	.1603	.1640	.0970	.2324	.1259	.2205
B09B	5.0029	.2318	.1651	.1797	.2366	.0674	.1194
B08K	4.4082	.2508	.1388	.1220	.3003	.1367	.0514
B08E	7.1826	.1509	.1279	.0963	.2728	.1380	.2140
B08B	4.8196	.2543	.1943	.0689	.3537	.0903	.0386
B07P	4.5305	.2124	.1902	.1574	.3275	.0722	.0403
B07B	4.5501	.1949	.1972	.1293	.2929	.1446	.0410
B06P	5.0288	.1973	.0726	.1342	.4388	.0280	.1290
B06K	5.4922	.2255	.1017	.1247	.1942	.2126	.1413
B06E	4.6865	.2416	.1006	.2571	.3446	.0179	.0383
B06B	5.9959	.1776	.1371	.1027	.4398	.0557	.0871
B05K	5.0183	.1914	.3777	.1057	.1363	.0584	.1304
B05E	6.0558	.1746	.1517	.0825	.2639	.2852	.0421
B05B	5.9696	.2661	.1156	.0808	.1751	.2854	.0769
B04P	5.0628	.2144	.1280	.2135	.2458	.0930	.1052
B04K	5.0151	.2226	.1381	.1238	.2542	.1441	.1172
B04B	6.1239	.1384	.0714	.0906	.4082	.2668	.0247
B03K	4.9718	.2329	.1830	.2083	.2446	.0000	.1313
B03B	4.1802	.2539	.1504	.2650	.2100	.0869	.0337
B02K	5.2181	.2114	.1441	.1617	.2058	.0879	.1892
B02B	5.1805	.2194	.1693	.1169	.3129	.1141	.0674
B01P	3.9901	.2410	.2064	.1060	.3683	.0602	.0180
B01K	4.8121	.2276	.1640	.1540	.3676	.0569	.0300
B01B	5.8151	.1431	.1842	.1632	.3649	.0811	.0635
-----	-----	-----	-----	-----	-----	-----	-----
MEAN	4.9552	.2173	.1575	.1440	.3098	.0920	.0794
(DOM)	4.1500	.2300	.1700	.1200	.4100	.0700	.0000
STD.D	1.9662	.1125	.1313	.2092	.1956	.2208	.1056

Figure 8   *Tabular output from the model, comparing maximum hourly heat loss $(W/m^2 °C)$ and component fractions (ρ) for the case study buildings with UK domestic figures (after Penz, 1983)*

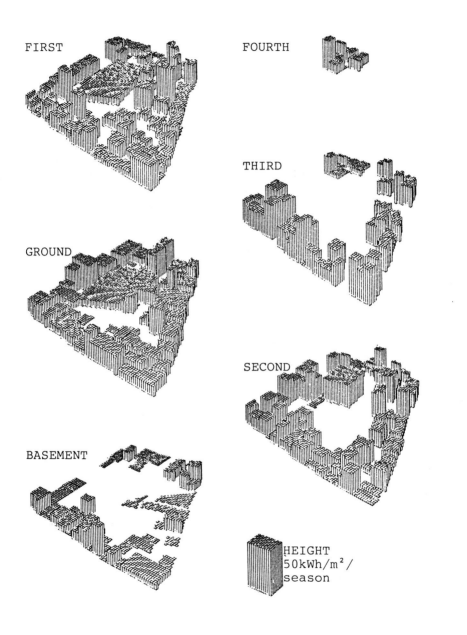

Figure 9   *The spatial distribution of net seasonal space heating demand, plotted with spatial data for each level of the built form sample*

predicted seasonal energy consumption of each of the premises. Predicted seasonal energy consumption was found to be within plus or minus 20% of all monitored fuel consumptions, with an average model discrepancy of 8%. The spatial distribution of net seasonal heating demand is investigated graphically in Figure 9, revealing a highly mixed and disparate sample at the room level of thermal analysis.

Conclusion

This paper has reported on a thermal network analysis technique which was developed specifically for handling data pertaining to a large number of urban buildings. The simplicity of the model and its construction enables particularly efficient utilization of computing resources, and the incorporation of spatial data facilitates analyses of complex built form configurations.

Some measure of confidence in the output has been gained through comparison with other published results and with monitored data. However, it is difficult to determine just what degree of empirical correlation constitutes an accurate model. This uncertainty is especially acute when simulating occupant behaviour and other largely unknown parameters, although a comprehensive survey of occupational characteristics significantly reduces the amount of unknown variables.

Because of the data handling ability of the statistical component of the model, variables may be readily transformed to represent hypothetical characteristics. The method therefore provides a useful basis for predicting seasonal energy flows of existing built form as well as those resulting from a variety of conservation strategies. In this way the analysis method provides a link between urban studies and detailed building energy analysis.

References

Gardner, P. (1984). *Energy Management Systems: Energy Technology Services 1.* London: The Energy Efficiency Office.

Matthews, L.J. (1985). *Energy Conservation in Central Urban Buildings.* Doctoral dissertation, University of Cambridge.

Nie, N.H. *et al.* (1985). *Statistical Package for the Social Sciences.* New York: McGraw-Hill.

Penz, F.A. (1983). *Passive Solar Heating in the UK Existing Housing Stock.* Report to the Energy Technology Support Unit, Harwell (Ref. ETSU S-1056a). The Martin Centre for Architectural and Urban Studies, University of Cambridge.

Uglow, C.E. (1981). The calculation of energy use in dwellings. *Building Services Engineering Research and Technology,* Vol. 2, pp. 1-14.

AN APPROACH TO THE ASSESSMENT OF THE ENERGY EFFICIENCY OF URBAN BUILT FORM

Peter A. Rickaby

Centre for Configurational Studies
The Open University

Abstract

This paper reports ongoing work at the Centre for Configurational Studies, and deals with blocks of development in the central areas of British provincial towns and cities. Opportunities for modifying these blocks are limited, and change is likely to be progressive rather than wholesale. Factors affecting the fuel demand of a central urban block include its shape and size, its orientation and position relative to neighbouring blocks, its overall form, the mix and distribution of floorspace within it, the thermal characteristics of the fabric, and the pattern of occupancy. An approach is described to the identification of fuel-efficient combinations of these factors through the use of solar envelopes, surface area to floorspace ratios, and winter to summer solar exposure ratios (weighted according to fabric properties). Identification of fuel-conserving built forms will allow the long-term incremental redevelopment of central areas to be directed towards fuel-efficient configurations. In the meantime, the study of urban built form will permit the improvement of the building stock models incorporated in urban-scale land use and transport models. Proposed local modifications, for example changes in floorspace mixes or densities, may then be tested at the urban scale, and vice-versa.

Introduction

The attention of research into energy-related aspects of the built environment has hitherto been focused at the scale of the individual building, or of the city as a whole. What has emerged from this work is that the interactions between buildings can be as significant as the individual buildings themselves (Matthews, 1985), and that accurate urban-scale energy analysis requires models of the performance of buildings in local groups and in stocks (Rickaby, 1985). This paper deals with one kind of localized group of buildings, which also forms a stock at the national scale: the central urban block in the British provincial town or city.

Matthews (1985) has investigated a number of central urban blocks and made detailed investigations of one Cambridge block which is typical of those found in towns and cities throughout the country. It is roughly rectangular, with street frontages oriented approximately north, south, east and west, and contains a large number of separate properties developed as a mixture of residential, commercial and retail uses to an overall gross plot ratio of approximately three, in four storeys of building plus some basements. The buildings are generally old and many-times adapted or extended from the original residential use: their fabric is thermally very poor and there are many separate heating systems. Some buildings are net importers of energy, others, at least at some times of the day, are net exporters of energy (for example, catering establishments). These observations are generally consistent with a visual survey of twenty English towns with populations between 50,000 and 150,000, carried out by the author in 1984.

A strategic approach to urban fuel efficiency

In the short term, improvements in the overall fuel efficiency of these buildings can be achieved by increased insulation, and by replacement of heating plant and controls with more efficient modern equipment. Opportunities exist for fuel savings to be made by inter-property collaboration within each block, for example by heat recovered from net heat exporters being supplied to net heat importers (Matthews, 1985). In the longer term, however, it will become important to achieve more fuel-efficient overall configurations for urban areas by altering the mix and location of urban land uses, and by modifying the forms of the developments that contain them.

The present form of many central urban blocks demonstrates that they have changed only slowly, over long periods. In some cases whole blocks have been swept away and redeveloped (particularly during the 1950s and 1960s), but in the majority of cases the multi-use, multi-tenanted character of central urban blocks results in slow and incremental development and adaptation. It is important, therefore, to identify fuel-efficient configurations of urban built form towards which incremental redevelopment can be directed by means of planning controls. Such controls would include target land use patterns and densities as well as bulk and location. Target configurations must not only provide fuel-efficient urban blocks, they must also be consistent with fuel-efficient land use and transport policies at the urban scale. The starting point in the identification of target configurations must of course be the existing configurations, and it will be important to consider overall architectural form in relation to heat loss, to direct and indirect insolation, and to the mix, density and location of uses within the blocks.

An important characteristic of existing urban built form is that central urban blocks occur in arrays - they are surrounded by other similar blocks, and adjacent blocks affect each other by shading. The nature of inter-block shading is determined not just by the form of the blocks but by the width and pattern of the streets (Gupta, 1984). In the central areas of many British provincial towns the street pattern is irregularly radiocentric, and focused around the confluence of six or more main routes which connect the town with its neighbours in various directions (Rickaby, 1985). In this sort of pattern it is not surprising that most central blocks are roughly trapezoidal in plan shape, and that nearly all of them have one elevation oriented within 30 degrees of south (see Figure 1).

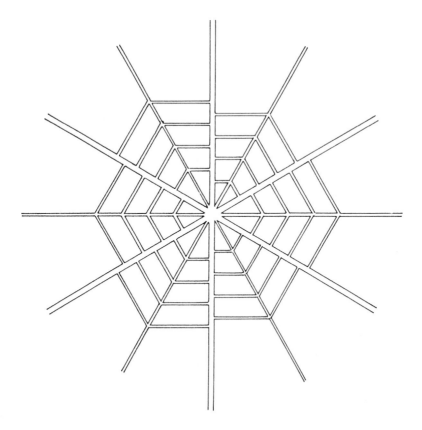

Figure 1   *An irregular radiocentric street pattern typical of British provincial towns*

A second characteristic is that many central urban blocks are 'hollow' - that is, buildings are concentrated at the perimeter, the central parts of the blocks being occupied by smaller buildings (often extensions of the perimeter buildings), or by courtyards. This is due to the necessity in most buildings of admitting daylight and natural ventilation, which tends to result in building plans only two rooms deep, and the need for service access to the rear of many types of commercial premises. The hollow pattern of perimeter development is not always followed, especially where blocks have been comprehensively redeveloped during the last thirty years, but it is a very common type. Such blocks have larger areas of external wall, relative to floorspace, than modern deep-plan blocks, and most buildings within each block have at least two aspects.

A principle that might be adopted in determining efficient urban block forms is that during the heating season the shading of any block by its neighbours should be minimized or eliminated in order to maximize the opportunity for the exploitation of direct solar gains (though in some cases shading may be desirable in order to reduce gains). Shading in arrays of blocks can be assessed by means of the techniques of 'solar envelope' construction developed by Ralph Knowles (1981), as illustrated in Figure 2. The solar envelope defines the greatest volume of development that can be placed on a given site without shading neighbouring sites, and it must be calculated by convention at some appropriate time such as noon on the winter solstice. In an urban context the form of the solar envelope will be determined by the pattern and width of the surrounding streets, and by the orientation and slope of the site. In many cases existing developments appear to break through winter solar envelopes, particularly on the northern sides of blocks, and so it is unlikely that idealized built form, wholly contained within the appropriate solar envelope, could be achieved for some considerable time, if ever. The solar envelope would not in any case be the sole determinant of block form, but would interact with other constraints, such as the requirements of access and density, to determine the overall form of the development.

Techniques for evaluating urban built form

Within the urban block, the mix and disposition of floorspace and built volume, the thermal characteristics of the building fabric, and the patterns of occupancy will all be significant in determining the overall efficiency of the development. Techniques are therefore required for the comparative evaluation of the options available for the

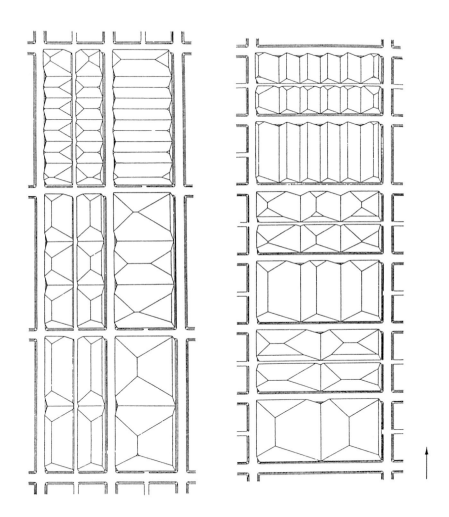

North-south subdivision of blocks   East-west subdivision of blocks

Figure 2   *Solar envelope of city blocks (source: Knowles, 1981)*

modification of both real and typical urban blocks. Such techniques will not only assist designers and policy-makers but also provide a means for understanding the energy-related characteristics of urban built form.

Some work on the problem of building shape and heat loss has been done by March, who has discussed the question "What shape should a building be to reduce heat loss?" and shown that for simple rectangular blocks with undifferentiated faces "the form that will minimise heat loss (not surface area) is the one whose *thermal image* is a cube such that heat losses through all three pairs of opposite faces (i.e. including the ground) are equal". March also points out that "it is misleading to suggest that forms which minimise surface area with respect to volume have any particular merit in terms of heat loss, or that measures of compactness which compare surface areas to volumes have any significant relation to thermal performance" (March, 1972).

This rather calls into question the most obvious indicator of the thermal efficiency of built form, the simple ratio of floorspace to surface area. This ratio provides some indication of the spatial efficiency of the enclosure, but it takes no account of variations in the thermal characteristics of building fabric, nor of the effects and directionality of solar gains. The floorspace to surface area ratio may be modified to take account of variations in fabric characteristics, by introducing elemental thermal transmissivities, but as an indicator of formal efficiency it is only really applicable to blocks which perform in what Hawkes (1982) has called the 'exclusive' mode, being a measure which takes account of heat loss from the block but not of solar gains or the resultant thermal balance.

When orientation and insolation are also taken into account, then the form that will minimize net heat loss (after solar gains) is the one whose *net* thermal image is a cube, and this form will change constantly with the movement of the sun! Hawkes (1982) describes buildings which exploit insolation to their own thermal advantage as buildings of the 'selective' mode. An approach to the assessment of insolation effects is that adopted by Olgyay (1963) in comparing the direct solar exposure of building forms in summer and winter. In Britain, in principle, solar gains are of use only in winter, when it is desirable to maximize them in order to reduce heating loads. In summer, gains are not generally useful and may lead to overheating, so it is desirable to minimize them. Thus for a particular block the ratio of summer insolation to winter insolation is of interest. Figure 3 shows an orthographic projection of a simple wire-frame model of the Cambridge block studied by Matthews (1985), as seen from the sun at noon on the summer solstice. Figure 4 shows the same model viewed from the sun at noon on the winter solstice. In each case we can measure the 'solar aperture' of the block as the area of its silhouette on the drawing, less the area of the courtyard, at the appropriate scale. The apertures are 4554 square metres and 2244 square metres respectively, and the summer:winter ratio is 2.03:1.

Figure 5 shows the summer solstice view of the 'regularized' version of the same block suggested by Matthews, in which the built form is a perimeter development 10.5 metres high and 15.6 metres deep. Figure 6 is the winter solstice view of the same block. In this case the apertures are 4012 square metres in summer and 2260 square metres in winter - a 12% reduction in summer and a 1% increase in winter, resulting in a summer:winter ratio of 1.78:1. This suggests that the regularized version of the block is a more efficient form than the original version, from the point of view of the sun.

Thus the summer:winter solar aperture ratio provides a crude technique for comparing the direct insolation characteristics of built form. Table 1 provides a comparison of the solar apertures calculated for the existing Cambridge block, the regularized 'ring' form, and a simple four-storey slab form (see Figure 7). A more sophisticated version of this technique would weight the apertures according to the areas and thermal characteristics of the elements of the visible fabric. Thus the presence of glazing exposed to the sun in winter but not in summer would be reflected in a lower summer:winter solar aperture ratio.

Built form	Solar aperture (m^2)		Summer:winter ratio
	Summer solstice	Winter solstice	
Existing	4554	2244	2.03:1
Ring	4012	2260	1.78:1
Slab	3244	1604	2.02:1

Table 1   *Overall solar apertures and summer:winter solar aperture ratios for the existing Cambridge block described by Matthews (1985) and two simple variants of its built form*

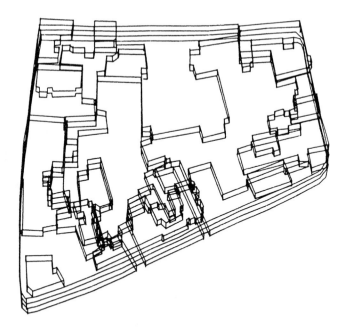

Figure 3   *An orthographic wire-frame view of the Cambridge block studied by Matthews (1985) at noon on the summer solstice*

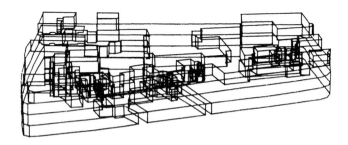

Figure 4   *An orthographic wire-frame view of the Cambridge block studied by Matthews (1985) at noon on the winter solstice*

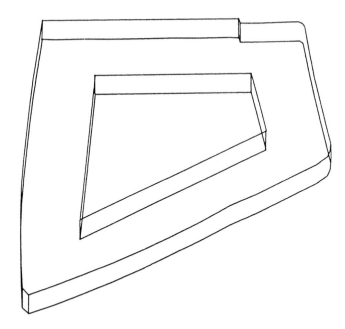

Figure 5 *An orthographic wire-frame view of a 'regularized' version of the Cambridge block studied by Matthews (1985) at noon on the summer solstice*

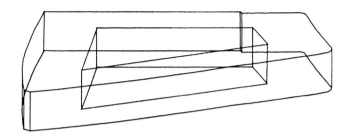

Figure 6 *An orthographic wire-frame view of a 'regularized' version of the Cambridge block studied by Matthews (1985) at noon on the winter solstice*

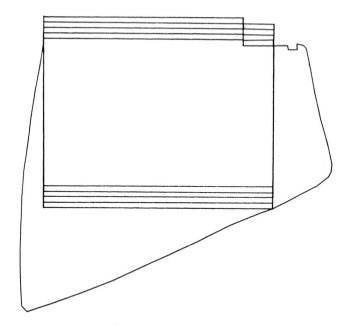

Figure 7   *An orthographic wire-frame view of the 'slab' version of the Cambridge block studied by Matthews (1985) at noon on the summer solstice*

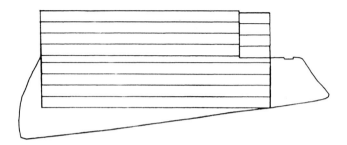

Figure 8   *An orthographic wire-frame view of the 'slab' version of the Cambridge block studied by Matthews (1985) at noon on the winter solstice*

However, this 'snapshot' technique has a serious limitation, as illustrated by Figure 7, which shows the summer solstice noon view of the same block redeveloped by a rather insensitive architect as a simple four-storey slab with elevations oriented squarely north, south, east and west. The east and west elevations are not visible; and the same is of course true of the noon view on the winter solstice (Figure 8). To overcome this limitation it is necessary to consider orthographic projections of the model as seen from the sun at hourly intervals from sunrise to sunset. Figure 9 shows this sequence of views at the summer solstice, and Figure 10 shows the sequence for the winter solstice. If in each case the solar apertures are calculated and plotted, as in Figure 11, then the areas under the curves may be defined as the summer and winter 'direct solar exposures' of the block, in square metre hours. The summer exposure is 40101 square metre hours, and the winter exposure is 10004 square metre hours, a ratio of approximately 4 to 1. (The dip which appears in the exposure curve at noon in each case is the result of the orientation of the block, neither of the side elevations being exposed at that time; and the dip would of course be less significant if indirect or diffuse radiation were also taken into account). A more 'solar-efficient' block would produce a lower ratio, and the curves would be closer together on the graph.

The measure of direct solar exposure provides a more sophisticated measure than the measure of solar aperture, and in principle it could be extended by automation to cover the complete heating season rather than just the conventionally adopted solstices. It also provides a means of investigating asymmetrical blocks, which produce asymmetrical exposure curves, indicating that solar gains are biased by the built form towards either end of the day. This is an effect observed by Knowles (1981) in the buildings at the Acoma Pueblo in New Mexico, and the principle is of course just as applicable in British town centres, even though the solar radiation is less intense.

Knowles has also suggested a measure of the 'efficiency' of built form that attempts to take into account both heat loss and direct solar exposure. This measure is the direct solar exposure divided by the overall surface area (Knowles, 1974). Blocks with large areas of roof and southerly elevations, relative to the area of northerly elevations, would be identifiable by high values of this measure. The ratio of the summer values of this measure to the winter values would reflect the amount of seasonal solar shading inherent in the built forms of the blocks.

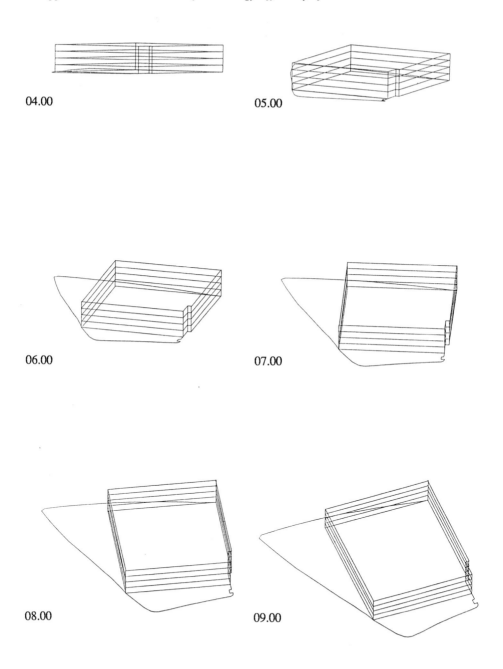

Figure 9   *The hourly sequence of views of the 'slab' version of the Cambridge block studied by Matthews (1985) between dawn and dusk on the summer solstice*

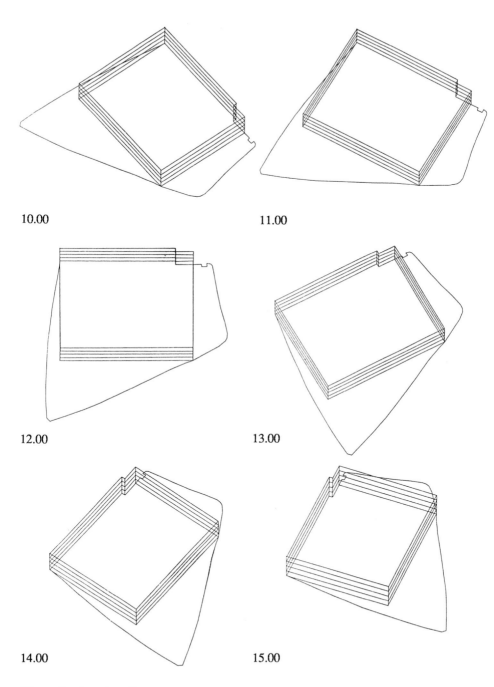

10.00

11.00

12.00

13.00

14.00

15.00

Figure 9 *(continued)*

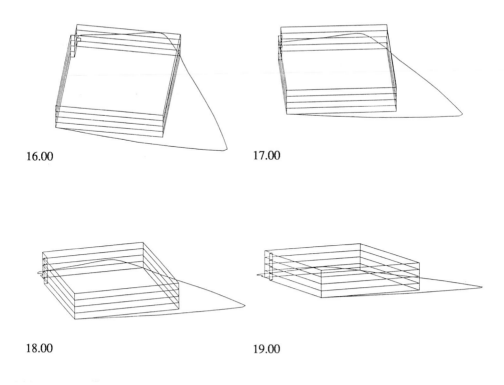

16.00   17.00

18.00   19.00

20.00

Figure 9   *(continued)*

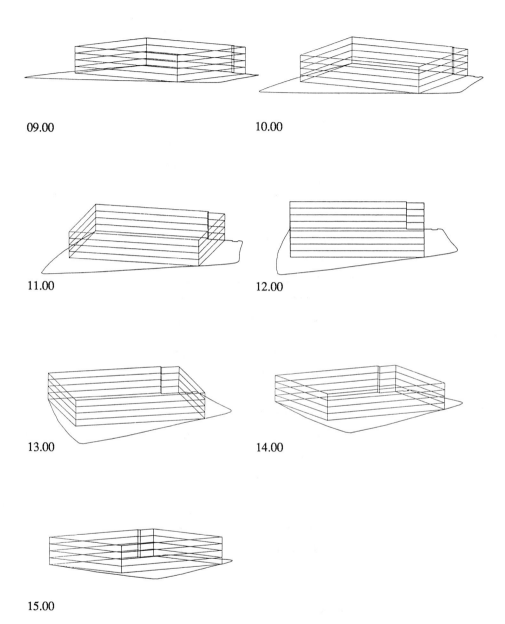

09.00

10.00

11.00

12.00

13.00

14.00

15.00

Figure 10 *The hourly sequence of views of the 'slab' version of the Cambridge block studied by Matthews (1985) between dawn and dusk on the winter solstice*

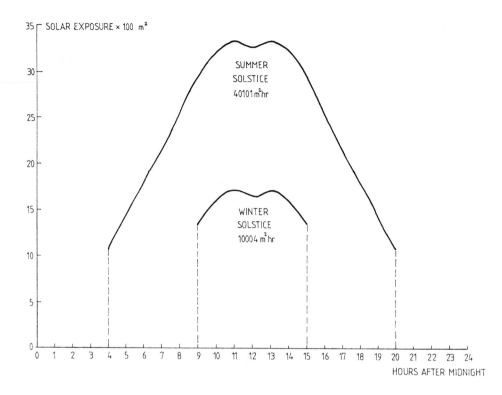

Figure 11 *The 'solar exposure' of the 'slab' version of the Cambridge block studied by Matthews (1985) plotted at hourly intervals at the summer and winter solstices*

The arrangement of uses within blocks

As Knowles has shown, the bias of solar gains towards roofs and southerly elevations can be exploited by the architect by adjusting the built form in order to concentrate gains in some areas and exclude them (by shading) from others. An examination of Matthews' (1985) data for the Cambridge block reveals marked differences in thermal characteristics between different types of floorspace (see Table 2). Catering establishments, for example, have internal heat gains approximately twice as great as those in offices ($60kWh/m^2$/season and $30kWh/m^2$/season respectively in the Cambridge block). To what extent this is due to the location of these uses within the Cambridge block, rather than to the nature of the uses themselves, is unclear, but it is reasonable to assume that different uses are associated with different heat gains and demands approximately as shown in the table. This suggests that, notwithstanding other locational constraints, some types of accommodation might deliberately be placed in exposed parts of the block (for example the upper floors on the south facade), while others are deliberately shaded. Restaurants should perhaps always be located on the shady south side of the street so that the sunny north side is available for more demanding uses such as offices and residences!

The mix of the various uses within the block is a factor affecting not only the overall gains and space-heating demands but also the viability of systems for local heat recovery and district heating systems. Such systems require the matching of demands and supplies both in quantity and in time, so, for example, an efficient mix might combine office accommodation and shops (heated during the day) with an appropriate number of small residential units (heated mostly during the evening and early morning), so as to produce a roughly constant local heat load finely tuned to the particular characteristics of the system to be used.

Type of use	Energy density	Heat loss	Heat gain	Heating demand
		(kWh/m^2/season)		
Retail	105	106.37	34.89	71.48
Catering	394	111.08	60.46	50.62
Residential	126	122.79	41.90	80.90
Offices	102	134.49	30.27	102.22
Entertainment	241	100.92	28.93	71.99
Miscellaneous	10	108.78	3.09	105.69
Whole block	173	121.27	39.55	81.72

Table 2 *Energy density, (i.e. total annual fuel use divided by floor area), seasonal heat losses and gains, and annual space-heating demand, by uses, of the existing Cambridge block (source: Matthews, 1985)*

The mix of uses in each individual block will also affect the overall efficiency of the urban area, and policies aimed at modifying the form of urban blocks may have unexpected effects at the urban scale, for example in altering densities or patterns of travel. There is much interest at present in commercial buildings which incorporate atria, and in the use of atria not only as spaces intermediate between the internal and external environments but also as spaces which are public or semi-public. This idea, in combination with the similar interest in enclosed urban arcades, suggests quite dramatic alterations both in built form and in patterns of movement within urban areas. It is therefore important to combine studies of urban built form with simulation of the performance of the overall urban area, using techniques such as those described by de la Barra and Rickaby (1982). Similarly, research at the urban and regional scales will suggest residential and floorspace densities with implications for the form of the urban block.

Conclusion

The measures and techniques described above can be used in the search for appropriate and energy-efficient urban built form. The methodology of this work involves first the study of existing urban blocks in order to determine their overall forms, thermal properties and occupancy patterns, and simulation modelling at the urban scale to establish possible or desirable changes in development densities and patterns of land use. The next stage is the identification of ways in which incremental redevelopment of central urban blocks may be directed in order eventually to achieve a range of more fuel-efficient built forms. The options available may then be comparatively evaluated using measures such as the overall plot ratio, the mix and density of uses (and resultant fuel-demand densities), the relationship with the solar envelope, the ratio of surface area to floorspace, and the ratio of summer to winter solar exposure per unit surface area. Knowledge gained from this exercise can then be used in two ways: to underpin planning and building control policies, and to improve urban and regional scale simulation models used for similar purposes.

References

de la Barra, T. and Rickaby, P.A. (1982). Modelling regional energy-use: a land-use, transport and energy-evaluation model. *Environment and Planning B*, Vol. 9, pp. 429-443.

Gupta, V.K. (1984). Solar radiation and urban design for hot climates. *Environment and Planning B*, Vol. 11, pp. 435-454.

Hawkes, D.U. (1982). Building shape and energy use. In D.U. Hawkes and J. Owers (Eds.) *The Architecture of Energy*. Harlow: Longmans, Construction Press.

Knowles, R.L. (1974). *Energy and Form: an Ecological Approach to Urban Growth*. Cambridge, Massachusetts: MIT Press.

Knowles, R.L. (1981). *Sun Rhythm Form*. Cambridge, Massachusetts: MIT Press.

March, L.J. (1972). Elementary models of built forms. In L. Martin and L. March (Eds.) *Urban Space and Structures*. Cambridge University Press.

Matthews, L.J. (1985). *Energy Conservation in Central Urban Buildings*. Doctoral dissertation, University of Cambridge.

Olgyay, V. (1963). *Design with Climate: Bioclimatic Approach to Architectural Regionalism*. Princeton University Press.

Rickaby, P.A. (1985). *Towards a Spatial Energy Model: a Theoretical Comparison of Energy and Accessibility in Regional Settlement Patterns*. Research Project Report, Centre for Configurational Studies, The Open University, Milton Keynes.

MULTI-SCALE ARCHITECTURE

Sergio Los

Istituto Universitario di Architettura di Venezia

Abstract

This paper addresses the problem of an architectural design directed towards improving both the environmental quality of urban spaces and their surrounding buildings, and the use of energy resources, at a micro-urban scale. Apropos the micro-urban scale, the argument is put forward that architectural design should be *multi-scale*; that distinctly separate levels of scale do not exist, but that each project itself should define its own scales and their relationships. Some investigations are presented which are intended to resolve these problems, and some projects illustrated in which the results are applied. In particular the paper considers the role of the language of design in the transfer of research results to architectural designers.

Premise

The theme of this seminar is energy conservation in design at the micro-urban scale. I will therefore try to frame my research in this context.

Rationalization of energy use is an interesting problem which highlights many inadequacies in architectural theory. It suggests the need to update methods in design, so as to improve the energy performance of buildings in the wake of the reduction in availability of oil. It poses questions such as:

How are the methods of designers normally changed? The artistic and architectural avant-garde of the Modern Movement set out to achieve something of this sort when they formulated new typological models and new procedures (in fact more models than procedures) to adapt their projects to the spirit of the time (to the changed conditions of industrial society).

How is expertise passed on from one designer to another, given that to change methods in design these must somehow be communicated? How can architectural design be taught? The experience of functionalism teaches us that we cannot update the scientific tools alone, in those areas where we know how expertise can be passed on; since in architectural design such tools are inextricably linked to processes of composition.

Two kinds of interconnected problem areas emerge:

> Updating of methods in design, seen as the normal condition of architectural culture.

> The reproduction of architecture in the schools, seen as the central question in design (as opposed to the individual design process).

This paper therefore treats the conservation of energy as just one of many concerns which create the need for an updating of design methods. In order to address the question of this updating, it poses the question of the reproduction of the institutions of architecture. The reproduction of architecture, by introducing periodic changes, itself constitutes the means by which this continuous adjustment of design methods is achieved.

These two questions, reproduction of architecture and updating of methods, have to do both with finished buildings and with design processes. They relate to the structural characteristics of the buildings, and to the sequences of operations in the processes of design. Evolutionary modifications have their consequences both for buildings and processes; these would be modifications of the buildings and modifications of the processes.

The evolution of buildings towards a new paradigm

Let us consider the changes which relate to the buildings, and try to identify the parameters or factors involved.

Architectural design at the micro-urban scale has in recent years become a central problem, through the importance which a number of topics have assumed in architectural thinking: the idea of *contextualism*, the sense of place, the specific character of architecture as a fixed extension of the site (something like the relation of a prosthesis to the human body), the mediation between ground-plane and project, the building process as a modification of the local environment rather than as the insertion of an object into the environment. The urban locality assumes a special typological importance as a subject for design, even for architects with quite different theoretical interests.

So all this allows us to formulate an approach to architectural design. The different scales of a project - interior design, building design, urban design - are not predetermined or immutable. Rather they become defined, on different occasions, in relation to the particular design problem, which establishes the relative autonomy of these levels of scale, and their relationships. This approach becomes clear if we consider the emergence, in the 1960s, of a new paradigm for architectural design: the network of connected urban spaces.

An interest in urban space as a subject for design characterizes, in the post-war period, the overthrow of functionalism as an international style, and its replacement by a typology of urban spaces which extended downwards from the scale of the city, as much as it was developed upwards from the scale of the building. This renewed interest on the part of architects in urban space, and this redefinition of the scale of intervention, translated into a set of alternatives in design, were the relevant factors in a contextual architecture which could finally resolve a fundamental problem for architectural theory: how to overcome the dichotomy between a contextual architecture with little theoretical basis and therefore not easily taught, and a different well-formalized architecture, easily imported in the schools, but an architecture of objects and therefore not properly integrated with those other historic architectures which constitute the city?

If we consider the four generations of designers whose work makes up the architectural culture of this century, we can get a sense of the problems of the present day and our possibilities for solving them (Figure 1).

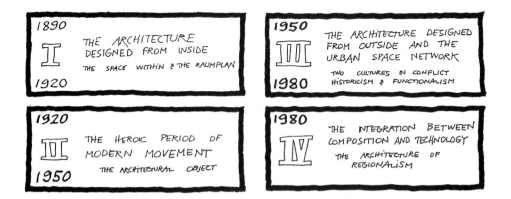

Figure 1   *The four generations of architectural design in the twentieth century*

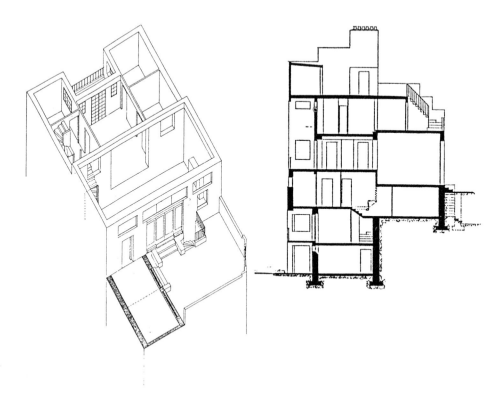

Figure 2   *Adolf Loos, house for Tristan Tzara, Paris (1926/27): the 'raumplan' concept*

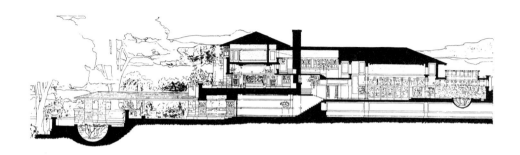

Figure 3   *Frank Lloyd Wright, house for Thaxter Shaw, Montreal, Canada (1906): the 'space within' concept*

The first generation discovered interior space and its complexity, reacting against academicism and formulating a contextual architecture integrated into the urban and rural environment. Various regional movements articulated these themes, in different ways, but characterized overall by a particular mode of experiencing interior space, which was expressed in a great variety of forms (Figures 2, 3).

The following generation was inspired by an intense ideological passion to remake the world. According to this idea, the past is overcome by a present which claims to replace it completely. There was therefore not the slightest interest in integrating new buildings into the pre-existing urban and rural context. Buildings would have to go through the kind of process of development which characterized the evolution of machines (aeroplanes, cars, ships, etc.). The new industrial technology was thought to have sufficient power to overcome any variations in local environmental conditions, and buildings became distinct self-referential objects (Figure 4).

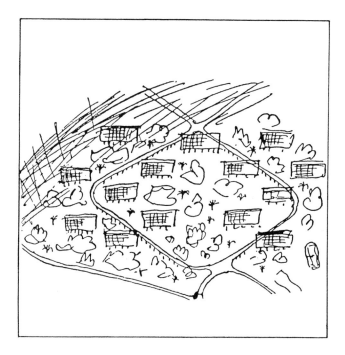

Figure 4   *Le Corbusier, 'Ville Radieuse' (1930): buildings independent from the system of public spaces*

In the 1950s, after thirty years in which the Modern Movement had given its attention in design above all to the built object, there came about a gradual shift in architectural conceptions of space, towards a gridded structure characteristic of urban spaces. From the self-contained object, epitomized by Bauhaus building, attention moved to a reticulated orthogonal system of spaces/streets, as represented by Louis Kahn's plan for Philadelphia (Figure 5).

To this transitional phase, brought about both by the rebuilding of the cities after the war and by immigration to the cities from the countryside, there were given many names, many emphases: from 'town design' to 'urban typology' or 'morphology', from 'contextualism' to 'the urban dimension of architecture'. In this climate of ideas there emerged a fascination with the components of the city, and there was developed a typology of urban spaces (Figures 6, 7).

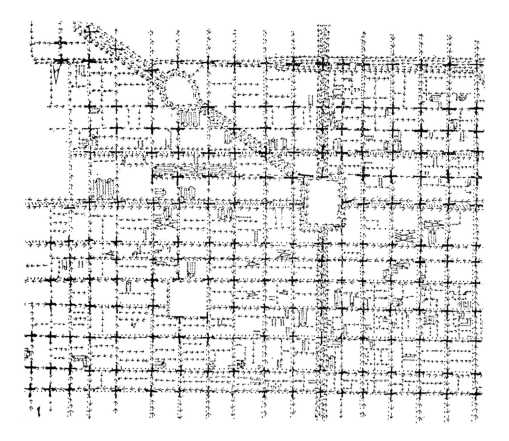

Figure 5   *Louis Kahn, Philadelphia center plan*

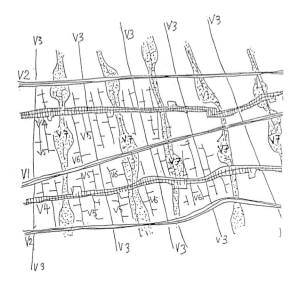

Figure 6 *Le Corbusier, 'The 7 ways': classification of different street types*

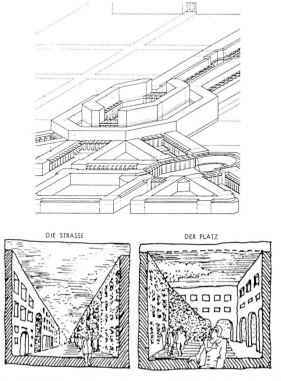

Figure 7 *Leon Krier, Leinfelden Centre, Stuttgart (1971): design of public space*

The shift of interest which characterized the evolution of architectural conceptions of space was represented in later projects which juxtoposed the built object and the network system of urban spaces (Figures 8,9).

This transition from built object to urban space was followed by Kahn in his rigorous separation of the two 'faces' of the building: the façade presented towards the exterior, which belongs to the urban space, and is internal to that space rather than external to the building; and the face presented on the interior, which follows the logic of the building, and is internal to *its* space (Figure 10). The rediscovery by Kahn and Scarpa of façades as walls of urban rooms (immediately taken up by Venturi and others, Figure 11) recalls the architectural experiments of Borromini, and more generally, those architects of the baroque who designed urban settings systematically as autonomous spatial realities, and not as mere leftover spaces (Figure 12).

The architects of the Modern Movement, by contrast, not only denied the building a façade - by considering all sides as equivalent - but they demanded an equation of exterior face with interior face, and a derivation of external appearance from plan in such a way that neither could be used other than in the particular combination arising in that building.

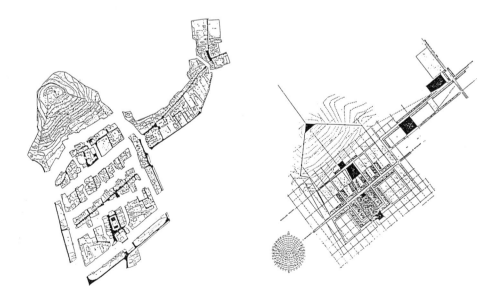

Figure 8   *Sergio Los, plan for historic centre of Marostica, Veneto, Italy (1968)*

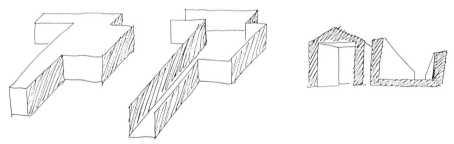

Figure 9 *Antithesis between built object and urban space network system*

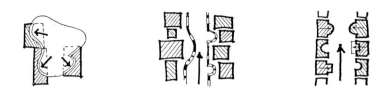

Figure 10 *Louis Kahn, design for the Angolan Consulate (1959): the façade as an interface between the building and the urban space*

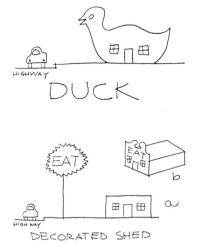

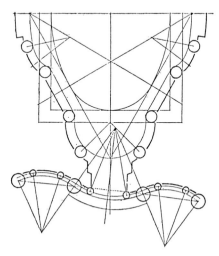

Figure 11 *Robert Venturi: the façade as decorated shed*

Figure 12 *Francesco Borromini, San Carlino: the façade as a component of the urban space*

The process of design

If we consider the changes which are important for the process of design, we discover an aspect which had become very much neglected by the systematic design methods movement, largely due to the fact that only the single project was considered, and not the evolutionary process in which many designers take part: and that was the question of *how design hypotheses are generated*. These hypotheses were imagined as being produced deterministically through a process of optimization, or else were thought to spring from the boundless creativity of designers. In truth, design hypotheses are generated out of the inherited language of architecture. It follows that, besides methods, it is also necessary to pass on, via teaching, this design language. This is the principal argument of my paper.

Let us now examine why we have to pass on not just the scientific tools of analysis, but also the language of design.

Recent research devoted to the problem of design at the micro-urban scale has been directed principally towards the kind of critical evaluation of projects which the culture of scientific methodology has emphasized for so many years. In this climate of ideas it was believed that, given the requirements and constraints, it was possible to find algorithms or procedures for determining the optimal form. It is possible to demonstrate that, on the contrary, from a logical point of view, while one may *de*duce the performance characteristics of a given design hypothesis, one cannot *pro*duce such hypotheses starting just from a statement of the performance requirements.

Given a case (the design hypothesis) and a rule (the simulation model) one may obtain by deductive inference the unique possible result (the performance characteristics of the given hypothesis). If instead, however, one defines the required result (the performance characteristics), there does not exist a mode of inference by which, using a given rule (a specific algorithm), one may determine uniquely the case (the design solution) (March, 1974).

There exist scientific procedures for deducing the performance characteristics of any specific project, no matter how it is designed in detail; but in order to pass, step by step, *from* the requirements, *to* a configuration in which those requirements are satisfied, it is necessary to proceed by an abductive mode of reasoning - that is, relying on a system of classification. For a given configuration there exists only one set of performance characteristics; but many configurations may offer the *same* performance characteristics, as laid down in the design specification.

If objective inference proceeds through a classification of these form/performance dualities, we must calculate for every form its corresponding performance. Then, to discover that form which best meets the given design problem, we identify the performance characteristics with those forms to which they are linked in the classification, and so move to an appropriate form. Since it is not possible to compute the performance of *all* conceivable forms, it becomes necessary to discover certain regularities, which allow us to limit the fields of possibilities within which we must carry out these calculations.

In order to explore the ranges of forms in a systematic way, and to isolate those parameters which allow us to reduce the multiplicity of combinations of form/performance, we have categorized the variety of building types in an organized way as a continuous sequence of configurations, such that every form constitutes a variation, by reference to well-defined parameters, of neighbouring forms in the sequence. By calculating the relative performance if these series of forms, it is possible to isolate certain recurring correlations which allow the reclassification of building types in energy and environmental terms. Once such a new classification is established, it is possible to generate configurations which satisfy given sets of performance requirements.

This study has been undertaken both at the building scale and at the urban scale. For the building scale, a housing module type has been defined, deriving from statistical analysis of the Italian housing stock and from current building standards. Different typologies have then been constructed, by combining a fixed number of those modules in various ways. By relating the performance characteristics to the parameter variations of the forms, it is possible to identify forms which offer satisfactory performance in energy efficiency terms. On this basis, particular projects, defined in greater detail, have been developed (Figure 13).

Also, for studying the environmental quality of urban space, various configurations have been generated made up from different combinations of a specified number of housing modules. The regularities discovered when the performance characteristics of these various types of urban space are measured relative to the parametric variations, have made possible a classification which decreases the level of uncertainty involved in any given project (Figure 14).

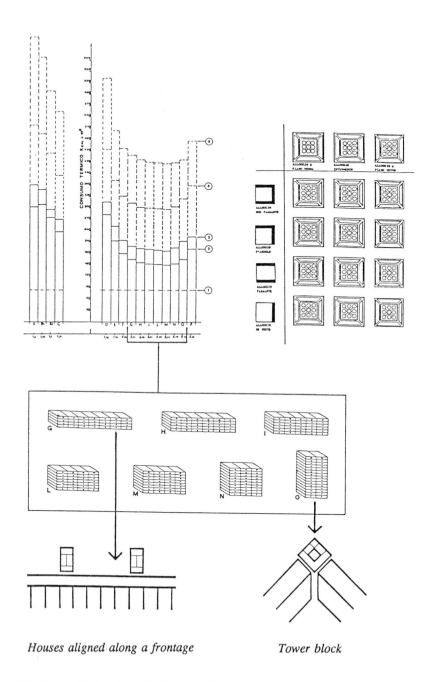

Houses aligned along a frontage   *Tower block*

Figure 13 *Centro Nazionale delle Ricerche, Progetto Finalizzato Energetica (CNR/PFE 1),
Sergio Los and others (1981): building morphology and energy behaviour*

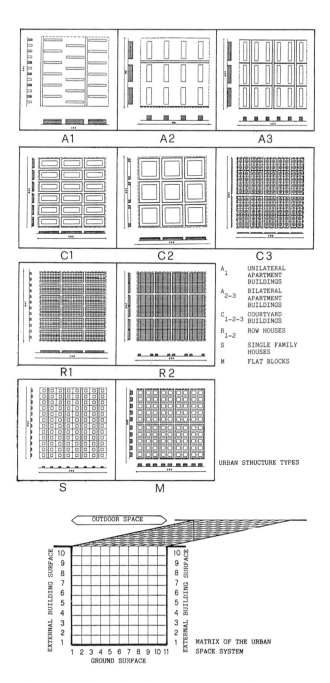

Figure 14 *Sergio Los (1983-84): a bioclimatic approach to the design of urban outdoor space*

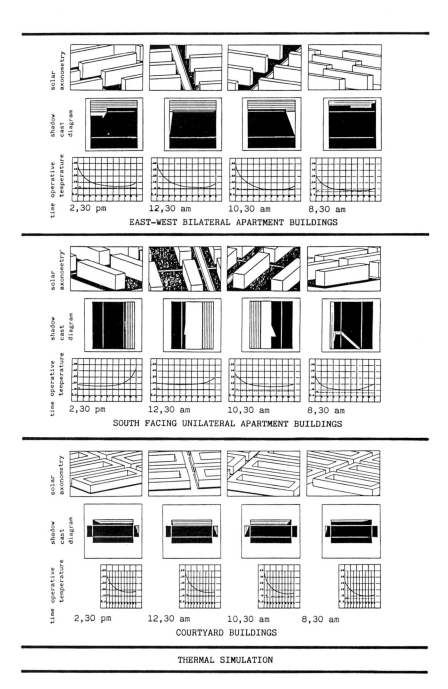

Figure 14 (continued)

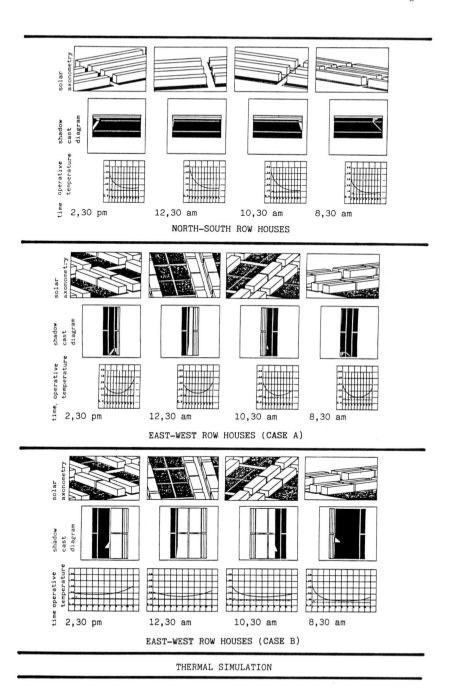

Figure 14 (continued)

By this means, designing proceeds almost completely on the basis of semiotic judgements, and thus on the basis of the expertise possessed by designers which is expressed in those judgements. The reliability of such semiotic judgements is assured by the existence of a code which relates the various forms employed in the project to their corresponding performance characteristics: for example, the form of a window is linked to the amount of light which it admits to a room; the cross-section of a column is linked to the load which it can carry; the width of a corridor is linked to the number of people who can pass along it. A project can progress in reasonable time, so long as designers can make all these semiotic judgements on the basis of their experience, without continual recourse to calculation.

But for this to come about, it is necessary for the language, and therefore the chosen standards which it embodies, to come to be communicated in the schools in a mature form, capable of being sustained by rational argument and capable of resolving problems, not just as a repetition of 'cliché'. The use of the typological method (or more simply, of typology) has, through its system of rules, allowed throughout the history of architectural culture the exercise in design of such semiotic judgements, so reducing the scope of judgements based on fact.

The study of design language, as a means of strengthening theoretical support for the typological method, is directed towards minimizing the need for performance evaluations carried out on the basis of factual judgements, which make the design process too costly. This was the central difficulty with systematic design methods which, starting from a *tabula rasa*, imposed an impracticable number of performance evaluations. The cost of design of a project, developed to satisfy the criteria set by all these evaluations, could never be repaid by all the benefits which derived from them. For this reason, in order to minimize the corrections to the design necessitated by such processes of evaluation, the project becomes *prestructured*, and so advances in a more satisfactory way on the basis of an architectural language, which incorporates the accumulated knowledge of a series of precedents in design.

In the intermittent updating of rules in the language of design, however, the cost of a large number of performance evaluations, and therefore of factual judgements, is perfectly acceptable, and is largely compensated for by the benefits which these bring. Here is the central concern of this paper: a method for updating the rules, through a study of the language of architecture, so communicating the results directly back into design for energy conservation.

When a modification of the contextual circumstances renders obsolete those semiotic judgements, which are based on a fixed code, it becomes necessary to make factual judgements based on processes of deductive inference, which consist in calculating for a given form its corresponding performance characteristics. But this process is very expensive and cannot be available to every individual designer. It is therefore essential that research institutes provide, on a regular basis, an updating of the codes, by means of procedures analogous to those described above. Following from this, it is important to find the tools best suited for transmitting these codes to designers.

Architectural projects

In presenting certain of my own projects in which these concepts have been formulated, the paper proposes an updating of the language of design relative to the position of the Modern Movement. Such a re-evaluation looks both to the production of architectural propositions, and to the environmental codes which underlie their conception.

The revival of the façade, bearing in mind its role in the definition of urban space, is one concern in the formulation of these propositions. Another is the modification of norms, related to the evolution of codes which are linked, through architectural type-forms, to new environmental and energy performance standards. This linkage is effected by means of a systematic exploration, through parametric studies, of fields of morphological possibility.

The projects which are presented and discussed here serve as propositions, expressed in the language of architecture, concerning different ways of achieving a satisfactory environmental quality in urban space and in buildings while at the same time achieving a more rational and efficient use of energy. The presentation of the projects is intended to demonstrate examples of the techniques used, but also to provide directly applicable typological models, which can be used to modify existing codes, and which can allow designers to formulate appropriate design hypotheses from the point of view of environmental quality and energy saving (Figures 15, 16, 17, 18).

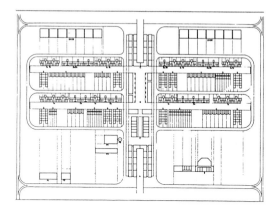

Different building types for various orientations

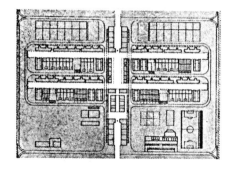

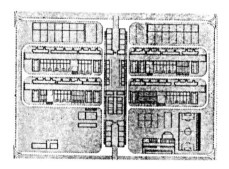

Pedestrian public space subsystem

Traffic subsystem

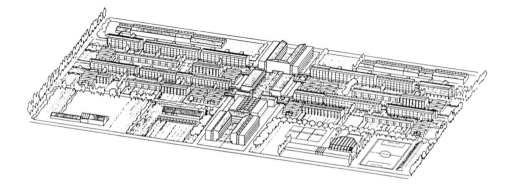

Figure 15 *Sergio Los, Natasha Pulitzer, Cepro srl: study for an application of ecological design techniques in a new settlement in Lombardy, Italy*

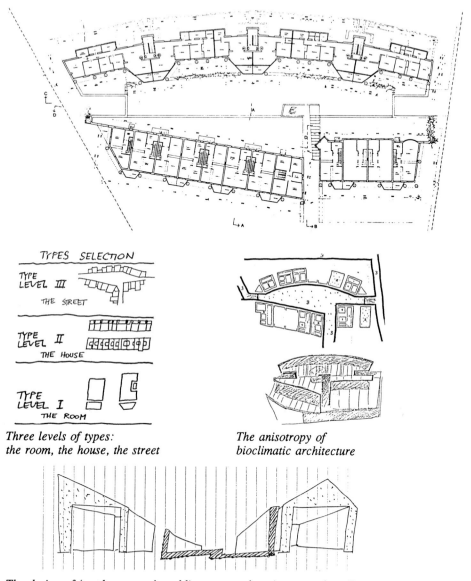

Three levels of types:
the room, the house, the street

The anisotropy of
bioclimatic architecture

The design of 'outdoor space': public space and environmental quality

Figure 16 *Sergio Los, Natasha Pulitzer and others (1984-85): demonstration bioclimatic
residential settlement in Lana, Bolzano, Italy. This project has been developed
on behalf of Centro Nazionale delle Ricerche - Progetto Finalizzato Energetica
(CNR/PFE 2) within the International Energy Agency Task VIII, research
activities*

South-oriented rear façade looking onto private gardens

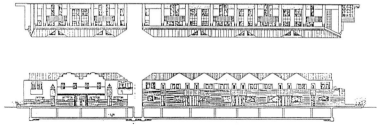

North-oriented main façade looking onto 'piazza'

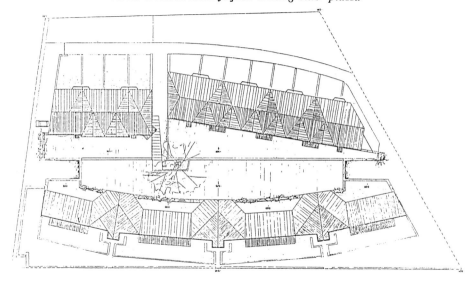

South-oriented main façade looking onto 'piazza'

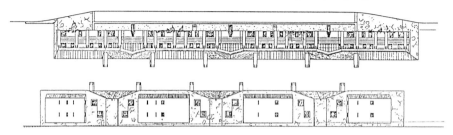

North-oriented back façade looking onto private space

Figure 17 *Anisotropy of the oriented urban system: the antithesis between solar oriented façades and façades looking onto the urban space*

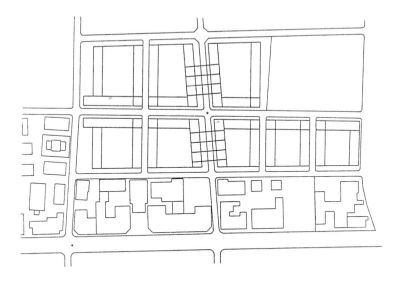

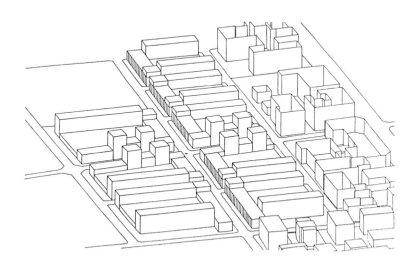

Figure 18 *Sergio Los, proposed reconstruction of a central area in Mestre, Venice, for public housing and commercial activities (1986). The whole configuration is determined by the oriented urban space network.*

Bibliography

Los, S. (1981). A bioclimatic approach to urban space systems. In *Proceedings*, International Passive and Hybrid Cooling Conference, Miami.

Los, S. (1981). The energy role in the reconstruction of the urban space system. In *Proceedings*, IEA International Conference on New Energy Conservation Technologies, Berlin.

Los, S. (1984). The design of urban outdoor space: a bioclimatic approach. In *Proceedings*, PLEA/84. Oxford: Pergamon.

Los, S. and Pulitzer, N. (1985). *L'Architettura del Regionalismo*, handbook on bioclimatic design in Trentino, Provincia Autonomia de Trento.

March, L. (ed.) (1974). *The Architecture of Form*. Cambridge University Press.

Pulitzer, N. and Los, S. (1985). *La Città del Sole: La Progettazione Urbana Ambientale-Energetica*. International conference and exhibition, Trieste, November.

PART 2 HOUSING AND BUILDING GROUPS

HEATPLANNER: A HOUSING STOCK ENERGY PLANNING TOOL

Malcolm Fergusson

Earth Resources Research Ltd., London

Mark Barrett

Energy Research Group, The Open University

Abstract

This paper describes the Heatplanner suite of computer programs, which are designed to aid in energy planning for given housing stocks. Heatplanner enables planners to assess the technical and economic consequences of proposed programmes of investment in energy conservation, efficiency and local energy distribution and supply. It is designed to be a practical tool for application rather than a model for the exploration of theoretical issues. The paper describes both the methodology and current applications of the model, and also possible future development.

History

The computer model upon which the present system is based was developed by Gerald Leach and Simon Pellew in 1982. It was designed to investigate energy use within the whole of the UK housing stock, and used survey sources to build up a detailed picture of that dwelling stock broken out by age, built form, main fuel type, heating type and tenure. A wide range of data sources was used to attribute realistic dimensions, fabric heat loss characteristics, ventilation rates and internal temperatures to each of the dwelling categories.

The main aim of the model was to determine current and potential future levels of insulation and other energy management measures, and to investigate their impact on UK energy demand. Integral to the model was a set of microeconomic calculations which were used to establish the economic viability of proposed measures. The methodology and results are described in detail in Leach and Pellew (1982).

Subsequently this model was modified to study the housing stock of Greater London exclusively, taking advantage of more detailed survey material available for that area. This version formed the basis of the Heatplanner system now in use at Earth Resources Research.

The purpose of the model

The primary aim of this model differs from that of many other domestic energy auditing models in that it is designed not to give the most accurate possible energy calculations for any individual dwelling, but rather to create a realistic if approximate picture of energy use within a large and mixed group of dwellings, which may be defined geographically, by age, by tenure, etc.

Furthermore it was developed as a tool to estimate both the costs and the benefits of a major national programme of energy conservation measures, rather than to model the current situation. As a consequence, a facility to introduce new conservation measures is a major feature of the model, and the financial implications of each such measure are calculated on the basis of fuel price and conservation cost parameters.

In practical terms, Heatplanner is intended to be used as a tool to help energy planners and policy makers evaluate the cost-effectiveness of a range of energy conservation investments in a given mixed housing stock. For example, it is currently being utilized to help local authority housing managers to formulate effective Housing Investment Programme (HIP) returns. It can also provide information necessary for the optimal design of local energy supply systems and for the development of wider energy strategies at the national level, as will be discussed in more detail below.

Since it is intended to be an easily used practical tool and to work within the limitations of the available data, the energy model at the heart of this system is itself relatively simple, and uses many simplifying assumptions with respect to the built stock under analysis.

Calculations used in the model

Typical U-values and building element areas, internal temperatures and ventilation rates for each category in the highly disaggregated built stock model are derived from a wide range of survey sources. Using a steady state model, the gross heat loads for ventilation and fabric loss are then derived quite simply from degree day data.

Hot water loads are calculated on the basis of the national average usage per occupant, allowing for differential water heating efficiencies within or outside of the heating season. Energy used for cooking is derived by a similar methodology, while that for sundries (primarily lighting and appliances) is a function of the number of hours of darkness, calculated monthly. Metabolic heat gains are calculated from average occupancy figures for each dwelling type, and from these figures the incidental heat gain is derived. This gives the intermediate space heat load which is the gross fabric and ventilation heat losses minus the sum of all seasonally constant incidental gains (all except solar gains).

The original version was based on a degree day model, in which Thom's method was used to derive degree days from monthly mean air temperatures and their standard deviations. Space heating requirements in terms of useful energy were calculated using a single zone steady state model. Air temperature figures for London are used in the current version of the program, whereas in the original version UK energy use figures were simulated by averaging the energy demands calculated using weather data for London and Glasgow in turn. Using this method, intermediate space heating requirements were calculated by multiplying the degree days by the specific loss factor.

The contribution of solar gain was estimated separately for south facing and other fenestration. South solar gain was derived using solar load ratio, utilizability factors and a storage:dump ratio; a method developed by Monsen *et al.* (1981). Non-south solar gain was calculated by the relatively simple methodology developed by Basnett (1975), and was assumed to be 80 per cent usable. This gave the total useful incidental gain, and from this net monthly energy loads for each fuel and use type were output.

The use of a steady state model based on degree days, while well validated and accurate enough for its original purpose, has certain major limitations in modelling changes in heating systems and heating regimes. In particular, the problems of modelling the use of electrical night-storage heating systems was perceived as a serious drawback of this method. Also the degree day methodology gives no indication of diurnal variations in heat load, and for this reason we have recently opted to switch to a diurnal simulation method, wherein internal temperatures, external temperatures, solar and other gains, and thus net heat loads can be calculated on an hourly basis for a typical day in each month of the year, and aggregated appropriately.

The key advantages which we perceive from this change are as follows:

i)   It will be possible to reflect a variety of heating regimes, and to move beyond the steady state method.

ii)   Changes in occupancy and appliance usage can also be reflected, with their consequent implications for incidental gains and space heating requirement.

iii)   It will be possible to model solar gain by a more straightforward method.

iv)   The system will be able to reflect the impact of night storage heating, and will be better able to model energy use in other housing types, such as those with passive solar design.

v)   Hourly energy demands are needed for the optimal design of energy supply systems.

The methodology adopted for this diurnal model is essentially quite straightforward, and is based upon the methodology previously described by Barrett (1982). Quantities of delivered fuel are simply calculated by dividing the net useful heat load by the appropriate heating system efficiency, giving fuel figures for each of the main fuels. These calculations are carried out for dwellings both before and after the addition of an energy management package, to determine the reduction in energy use which is likely to result.

Fuel costs and typical unit costs for a range of insulation measures are also input to the model, and from these it is now possible to calculate both the capital costs of conservation investments and the reductions in running costs which result from the measures chosen. These are then combined using discounted cash flow techniques to give estimated payback times and internal rates of return for the energy conservation package selected.

Data sources used in the model

A major difficulty with this type of model is that the structures of the data from the various sources differ, and often a variety of datasets have to be combined to obtain a reasonably full description of the housing stock. All the datasets used are from sample surveys of housing stocks in particular areas. For London, information from the National Dwelling and Housing Survey (NDHS) can provide statistically significant information down to borough level, splitting out housing data according to built form, tenure, rating code and central heating ownership. The Greater London Housing Conditions Survey (GLHCS) contains information for the Inner London area about numbers of dwellings using each main fuel, with wall and loft insulation, for each built form and tenure type, distinguishing between dwellings with and without central heating. Audits of Great Britain (AGB) produce surveys of double glazing ownership by built form and age of dwelling.

These three datasets are combined to give a comprehensive cross breakdown of most key energy characteristics of the housing stock. Average figures on occupancy, average internal temperatures, dwelling dimensions, etc., are then attributed to each housing category using information from a wide variety of sources, which are described in detail in Leach and Pellew (1982).

This methodology, while appropriate to the level of detail available on the UK housing stock, has obvious limitations and involves a number of undesirable oversimplifications. For example, it is often necessary to apply a global average for a given parameter to each category of building owing to the lack of more accurate data, even when there are good reasons for suspecting that there will be significant differences between houses of different ages, built forms, tenures, etc. This is especially the case for floor area, ventilation rate and average internal temperature.

Recent applications of the model

The Southwark Combined Heat and Power Scheme

Recently the model was used to investigate the energy characteristics of a number of large housing estates in the London Borough of Southwark, as part of a feasibility study for a new Combined Heat and Power (CHP) scheme. The purpose of this part of the study was to assess the expected monthly heat loads and peak winter demands for the four main groups of local authority housing estates which were under consideration for inclusion in the core of the scheme, and to investigate the economics of incorporating a package of energy conservation measures into the installation programme. Such calculations were clearly crucial for both the sizing of the proposed boiler plant, and for the assessment of the expected economic viability of the whole project.

It was of particular importance to establish the likely base load for the heating season as a whole, and the ratio of the peak demand to this base load, as this would determine what proportion of the heat required could be supplied by the main CHP boiler plant, and what proportion by top-up boilers which do not generate electricity. It was felt from the outset that an insulation programme was likely to change this ratio in favour of the CHP boiler, and thereby to improve the economics of the scheme; but as the housing estates in question comprised over one hundred blocks of flats and maisonettes of varying sizes and up to ten different construction methods, there were many difficulties involved in accurately assessing such factors.

It was therefore decided to model the estates on a block by block basis, using a number of simplifying assumptions and a slightly modified version of the central module of the Heatplanner system. To save time and resources, it proved possible in many cases to model a number of blocks simultaneously on account of similarities in their sizes and method of construction. Each block or group was modelled according to a set of 21 key parameters which were deemed to describe the block reasonably well, and which are shown in Figure 1. As can be seen, each block was modelled as a single entity, with due regard to its orientation, and some allowance where necessary for the existence of unheated lobbies, stairwells or liftshafts within the block.

Taking this simplified approach, it was essential to calibrate the predicted results of the model against true historical data as closely as possible. Fortunately the estates in question were all served by district heating (DH) systems, which not only ensured fairly consistent heating regimes and internal temperatures across each estate, but also gave us access to consolidated and accurate fuel use statistics for each estate on a monthly basis. In all cases, we found that the figures produced by the model for monthly energy demand agreed well with the actual fuel use statistics, when due allowance was made for system efficiencies, mains losses and the irregularities of the actual monthly temperatures from year to year. It seemed probable that in most cases the internal temperature derived from the calibration run was within one degree centigrade of the actual temperature for each block during the coldest months.

Having calibrated the model for each estate in this way, the next stage was to assess the expected annual and peak loads, without any additional energy conservation measures, but with the higher internal 24-hour temperatures specified for the upgraded system. As shown in the output tables in Figure 2, the output from such a run consists of monthly and annual heat loads in gigajoules, plus the peak demand rating in kilowatts. The latter represents the demand created by a constant external temperature of -1 degree C, which is the central criterion used by engineers in assessing the boiler capacity required by the system.

```
Bampton Estate

Int.temp.            17          (degrees C)
Main fuel            2        (1 Gas, 2 Elec, 3 Oil)
S/H.Eff.             .8
W/H.Eff.(S)          .7
W/H.Eff.(W)          .7
Wall U-val(1)        1.25
Wall U-val(2)        0
Loft U-val           1.42
Floor U-val          .6
Glazing U-val (D)      4.9
Glazing U-val (N)      4.4
Air changes/hr       1
Height               29.7        (of dwelling, m.)
Floor Area           308         (m^2)
Wall area(1)         1925        (external opaque wall area, m^2)
Wall Area(2)         0
Window area          997.2       (total,m^2)
   S-facing          290.4       (m^2)
   N-facing          45.7        (m^2)
Num occupants        126
Hot water/occ        45          (litres/cap/day)
Freezers/dwg         22          (av.no.per dwelling)
Gross-up factor      8
```

Figure 1   *Heatplanner input*

The final phase of the study was to assemble a package of energy management measures for each block type which would individually meet a specified internal rate of return on investment. Fortunately, the target internal temperature was specified quite independently of any energy conservation measures applied, which made it possible for us to consider each of our conservation measures to establish whether it would meet the financial criteria laid down. The selected measures were then applied together in a final run to calculate their impact upon annual and peak heat loads.

In brief, the results of this exercise had potentially far-reaching implications, as the high internal temperature specification (18 degrees C over 24 hours) produced favourable results for a wide range of insulation options. In almost all cases additional loft insulation and draughtstripping proved very attractive, and cavity filling was also financially viable in

```
HEAT LOSS AND ENERGY CONSUMPTION      Block  : NEW PLACE A
                                      Option : Run E - Full Package


    HEAT LOSSES
       loft              289.8        120.8 W/degK
       walls            2259.0        753.0 W/degK
       windows          3383.0       3383.0 W/degK
       floors            483.0        483.0 W/degK
       ventilation      2019.6       1009.8 W/degK
       total specific   8434.5       5749.6 W/degK

    FUEL USE
       space heating    1667.7       1101.6 GJ
       water heating     369.8        369.8 GJ
       cooking           428.5        428.5 GJ
       appliances        115.0        115.0 GJ
       overall total    2581.0       2014.9 GJ
       total electric    115.0        115.0 GJ
       total gas        2466.0       1899.9 GJ

    FUEL COSTS
       electricity cost  664.5        664.5
       gas cost        10517.5       8103.2
       total cost      11182.1       8767.8


               HEAT LOAD
    MONTH    Before   After    Gross-up

     Jan     343.9    242.1    1452.3   GJ
     Feb     303.4    212.1    1272.3   GJ
     Mar     284.6    198.1    1188.5   GJ
     Apr     215.5    149.5     897.1   GJ
     May      31.5     31.5     188.9   GJ
     Jun      29.8     29.8     178.8   GJ
     Jul      29.4     29.4     176.3   GJ
     Aug      28.0     28.0     167.9   GJ
     Sep      28.4     28.4     170.6   GJ
     Oct     165.0    116.0     695.9   GJ
     Nov     260.1    182.7    1096.1   GJ
     Dec     317.9    224.0    1343.8   GJ

     Peak    160.3    109.2     655.5   KW


    Total installation cost    52160.4
    Gross energy saved (GJ)     3396.4
    Gross cost saved ( /yr)    14485.7
    Payback (years)                3.6
    IRR                           27.8
```

Figure 2 *Heatplanner output*

many suitable block types. On a typical estate, we found that a total expenditure of £124,800 would pay back in 2.33 years, and reduce the peak heat load by over 19 per cent. Overall, economic energy management measures were estimated to reduce the peak load by 29 per cent.

The potential of this approach to energy auditing for the development of CHP and other local energy distribution schemes is considered further below.

Local authority energy plans

It is well known that energy conservation in the domestic sector is in many cases a good investment; the key problem is to overcome the institutional and financial obstacles to its implementation. For this reason Heatplanner is currently being used to develop energy conservation programmes for three London local authorities. The aim is to see how energy conservation measures can be integrated into a borough's normal house building, repair and maintenance activities, primarily within the local authority housing sector.

This work entails the collation of data on the public and private housing stock and the use of Heatplanner to identify a conservation programme offering the best improvements in thermal comfort for given investments. The scale of these investments, and of the concomitant building works, can be quantified by Heatplanner as an essential first step in the creation of such an energy conservation programme.

These investments, for both private and public housing, can then be integrated into the borough's Housing Investment Programme (HIP) and implemented as part of the normal repair and maintenance programmes of the housing department. Hence Heatplanner is here serving to develop policies for an institution that has the resources and powers to implement such programmes, and as a consequence there is a good chance that the energy conservation measures modelled by this system will actually be carried out.

Future developments: refinements and integration

Heatplanner is being developed by refining the program itself and by integrating it with other models.

Current modifications

Modifications to Heatplanner currently under way include:

i)   Extending the number of types of heating system dealt with;

ii)   Changing from degree day to hourly calculations to improve the modelling of certain heating systems (eg. passive solar and off-peak electric) and to output hourly loads which can be input to a local energy supply model;

iii)   Generalizing the model to include non-domestic buildings. Little work has been carried out on this change as yet.

Model integration

Urban buildings form part of a larger system of energy demand and supply. Different urban energy plans have different technical, economic, social and environmental implications both locally and nationally (and indeed internationally). This is especially so in the UK where energy supply systems are integrated at the national scale.

National energy planning should therefore take full account of the energy demand and supply system and aim to balance the investment of resources in different parts of this system. For example, an urban renovation programme which included energy conservation measures would directly and rapidly reduce the need for energy supply both in terms of peak capacity and of annual quantity supplied. In order to model the likely impact of such changes in policy upon the environment, the electricity supply system, etc., it is intended to integrate the Heatplanner program suite with other models which we have developed.

Thus in the CHP case study described above, Heatplanner was used to estimate total and peak heat loads and their seasonal distribution. This information, in conjunction with heat load density and a diurnal load distribution, can be fed into a model of the CHP system. The CHP model calculates the electricity generated in each hour and the fuel consumed. The electricity generated is converted to load duration form and is input to a model of the electricity supply system. This procedure has been carried out previously (Barrett, 1983), but the transfer of information from one model to another was not automatic.

Heatplanner currently deals with the temporal distribution of energy flows, however the spatial density of demand can also be an important determinant of the economics of energy supply systems where energy from one or more sources is distributed through a network to consumers. Most UK energy is delivered through such networks. In general the lower the density of energy demand, the larger are distribution costs as a proportion of the total cost of supply. Furthermore, the spatial density, orientation and built form of housing can constrain the potential use of distributed renewable energy sources, particularly of solar energy through passive and active collection systems.

The housing stock datasets, augmented with similar information on non-domestic buildings and, ideally, with information on building orientation, could be used to estimate the energy load densities and solar potential of specified urban areas. Owing to the availability of relatively accurate and detailed survey data for this area, it seems likely that London will be our first choice for further modelling developments.

References

Barrett, M. (1982). *A Dynamic Physical Energy Model of the United Kingdom.* Energy Research Group, The Open University, Milton Keynes.

Barrett, M. (1983). *The Development of Combined Heat and Power with District Heating in London. Report 6: The Impact of CHP/DH on the Electricity Supply System.* Greater London Council Report No. 278/1/R6.

Basnett, P. (1975). *Estimates of Solar Radiation falling on Vertical Surfaces from Measurements on a Horizontal Plane.* Capenhurst: Electricity Council Research Centre.

Leach, G. and Pellew, S. (1982). *Energy Conservation in Housing.* London: International Institute for Environment and Development.

Monsen, W., Klein, S. and Bechman, W. (1981). Prediction of direct gain solar heating system performance. *Solar Energy*, Vol. 27, pp. 143-148.

PASSIVE SOLAR SCENARIOS FOR THE UK DOMESTIC SECTOR

François Penz

Faculty of the Built Environment
Polytechnic of the South Bank

Abstract

The Martin Centre for Architectural and Urban Studies carried out a detailed survey of a representative sample of the housing stock of Cambridge as part of a project for the Department of Energy. Its purpose was to evaluate the potential within the domestic sector to exploit passive solar energy for space heating. An energy model of the existing domestic sector was built on the University of Cambridge main frame computer using an adapted BRE steady state calculation method, and each sample dwelling was assessed in terms of thermal load. Three types of retrofit were then considered: conservatories, roof collectors and Trombe walls. One of these passive solar systems was ascribed to each house in the sample with a potential, and thermal performances were derived from a graphical method based on detailed case study analysis using dynamic thermal modelling. A range of scenarios was then tested using the energy model of the Cambridge housing stock to assess the possible impact of the use of passive solar energy on UK domestic sector primary energy requirements. Some energy conservation measures were also evaluated and are presented as a background to the passive solar scenarios.

Introduction

In 1980-81 a survey of the housing stock of Cambridge was carried out by the Martin Centre as part of a project sponsored by the Department of Energy (ETSU). Its main objective was to determine the potential of the existing housing stock to exploit passive solar energy for space heating. 413 dwellings were surveyed as a representative sample of the 39,000 houses of the Cambridge stock. Data collected covered the physical characteristics of the dwelling, site information, energy use and pattern of occupancy. Around sixty pieces of information were gathered for each dwelling and were processed on the University's main frame computer using the SPSS statistical package.

The first task was to establish that the Cambridge survey was representative of the national picture. In general it was found that the Cambridge figures for age characteristics were broadly in accordance with national figures as shown in Table 1.

Age categories	Number of dwellings	Cambridge housing stock %	UK housing stock % (Source: Leach, 1981)
Before 1900	80	19.4	16.3
1900 - 1918	47	11.4	14.1
1919 - 1939	108	26.2	21.5
1940 - 1963	93	22.5	35.2
1964 - 1969	38	9.2	
After 1970	47	11.4	12.9
Total	413	100.0	100.0

Table 1   *Age characteristics of sample of Cambridge housing stock*

Some discrepancies were noted in the breakdown by dwelling type which includes fewer detached houses than the national figures. Also, in terms of floor area the houses in Cambridge were on average slightly larger than UK figures but overall there was enough confidence in the Cambridge sample to be able to extrapolate scenarios at the national level.

Solar characteristics of the Cambridge Survey dwellings

It was assumed that dwellings with a side facing ±45° of south were potential candidates for passive solar retrofit. Overall it was found that 61.7% of the dwellings had a potential and that semi-detached houses were the most suitable type, of which slightly more than two out of three could accommodate a retrofit (see Table 2).

In terms of age groups, it appeared that a greater potential existed in the 1919-1939 category, where 74% of the houses were suitable. This could have been a consequence of the 1919 Regulations concerning sunlight penetration in dwellings and the '12 houses per acre' planning law enforced at the time. In broad terms the 1919-1969 period seems to have been more favourable to southerly orientation than any other, certainly coinciding with lower density construction trends.

Dwelling categories	Number suitable	% of total suitable	% of the total stock	% suitable in category
Terrace	62	24.3	15.0	48.8
Terrace-end	24	9.4	5.8	53.3
Semi-detached	89	34.9	21.5	70.0
Detached	30	11.7	7.3	78.9
Bungalow	7	2.7	1.6	77.8
Flat	38	14.9	9.2	61.3
Maisonette	5	2.0	1.2	100.0
Total	255	100.0	61.7	

Valid cases = 413 dwellings

Table 2   *Dwelling types with a south side (±45° of south)*

With respect to overshadowing, 23.1% of the houses were found unobstructed and 71.4% of the total sample did not suffer more than a 10% reduction in collected solar radiation (average data over the heating season). The most common causes of obstruction were found to be buildings and trees. Certainly the most severe cause of overshadowing, cutting out up to half of the solar radiation, was found to be large trees, mostly in relation to pre-1939 detached houses. Finally, overshadowing appeared to be related to increased density, especially in the 'over 80 dwellings per hectare' category. A large proportion of these dwellings have their potential solar collection reduced by over 20%.

Passive solar performance assessment

First, an assessment of the thermal load of the Cambridge housing sample was performed using a steady state model devised by the Building Research Establishment (Uglow, 1981) to assess domestic energy consumption and the effect of improved insulation on existing dwellings. A computer version of this thermal model was built on the University main frame computer and each house in the sample was assessed in terms of thermal load.

In parallel a method was developed (Penz, 1984) to assess passive solar retrofit performances according to level of insulation, pattern of occupancy, orientation and overshadowing. This method was based on a number of case studies using a finite

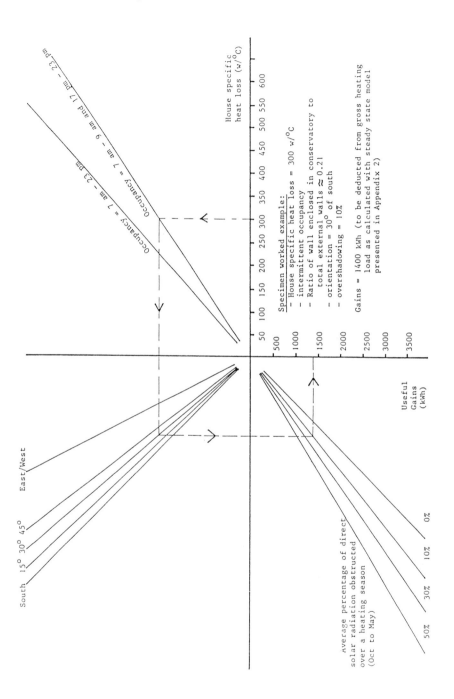

Figure 1   *A graph to assess conservatory retrofit gains*

difference hourly computer model. A simple graphical method was subsequently generated from the results in order to cope with the large number of houses in the sample. Graphs were generated for conservatory, Trombe wall and roof collector retrofits as illustrated for conservatories in Figure 1.

Suitability of passive solar systems to Cambridge Survey dwellings

Having established a way to determine passive performance, the next task was to attribute a retrofit to each house. In order to do so, photos of south facades as well as Ordnance Survey maps were used. One of the criteria to determine the best retrofit for a particular house was that every time more than one choice was technically feasible, preference would be given to the conservatory. For example, if the back of a terrace house could accommodate both a conservatory and a roof collector, only the conservatory would be considered. Roof collectors were attributed to dwellings with heavy obstruction at ground floor level and in general, in need of roof repair (e.g. typically the street side of a pre-1919 terrace house). Trombe walls seemed best suited to blank end-terrace walls or to the south side of a block of flats with very few openings (see Figures 2, 3 and 4).

Having 'retrofitted' each suitable house, the results shown in Tables 3, 4 and 5 were computed. The tables show that a large proportion of the existing housing stock could accommodate a passive solar system and that by far the largest category of retrofit would be conservatories with 39.7% of the sample. This is, of course, a consequence of the criteria set up to select the types of passive solar retrofit which clearly favoured the choice of conservatories whenever feasible. If this figure was applied to the UK housing stock as a whole, the total potential for conservatory retrofits would include over 8 million dwellings. The majority of these (65%) would be attributed to backs of terrace and semi-detached houses. In fact, 36% of the conservatories could be retrofitted to semi-detached houses which have a greater potential than terrace houses with 29% (including end-terrace). This is because semi-detached houses sometimes have frontages with gardens suitable for conservatory retrofits, while in general the high density in terrace house construction would not allow this.

Figure 2　*Back of a semi-detached house suitable for a conservatory retrofit*

Roof collectors, which represent a 13.3% potential in the Cambridge housing stock, are most suitable in pre-1919 terrace houses, and semi-detached houses mostly pre-1939 with hipped roof.

Trombe walls would have a maximum potential of 8.7% which is not negligible. It was found that flats of less than four floors would be most suitable as well as, of course, some end-terrace houses.

Figure 3   *The south facade of the semi-detached house is heavily obstructed but the hipped roof is clear and suitable for a roof collector (18 m^2 on average)*

Figure 4   *End-terrace: obvious candidate for a Trombe wall retrofit*

	% of total stock	Number of dwellings
Conservatory	39.7	164
Roof collector	13.3	55
Trombe wall	8.7	36
No side to south	38.3	158
Total	100	413

Table 3   *Breakdown of suitably orientated dwellings (± 45° of south) according to type of passive system*

Passive solar scenarios

A number of passive solar scenarios were modelled concurrently with a range of energy conservation assumptions based on a report by Leach and Pellew (1982). No attempts were made to model the growth and change in the housing stock through new building and demolition. Consequently, the results described below represent an assessment of future energy policies based on present day circumstances.

In order to cope with the wide range of possible energy scenarios, a number of high and low cases were assessed both in the energy conservation and passive solar fields. Leach and Pellew (1982) give two basic alternatives as shown in Figure 5 for the year 1990. The upper line corresponds to a low energy conservation scenario which follows the current trend of the Building Regulation standards. The prediction for 1990 is that the energy savings due to the wider spread of insulation measures in the existing stock would be offset by the increase in central heating ownership evaluated at 75% of all households. This explains why the line is horizontal. The lower line corresponds to a high energy conservation case, where the relevant dwellings have high levels of loft and cavity wall insulation and double glazing. Two more scenarios are then considered as shown in Figure 6 examining the effect of 100% central heating. The dates on the x axis are referred to as X and Y which represent points in time anywhere within the next 15 to 30 years.

The likelihood of having a 100% centrally heated housing stock might theoretically be realized by the year 1994 if the present growth of about 3% per year is sustained (Leach and Pellew, 1982). For the purpose of simplification it was assumed that gas would be the

Dwelling categories	Conservatory %	Roof collector %	Trombe wall %	No side to south %
Terrace	8.0 (21)	5.0 (35)	1.0 (15)	16.0
Terrace-end	3.0 (8)	1.0 (10)	1.0 (12)	5.9
Semi-detached	14.0 (36)	5.0 (35)	2.0 (20)	9.8
Detached	5.0 (14)	2.0 (13)	1.0 (9)	1.2
Bungalow	2.0 (4)	0	0.0 (0)	0.2
Flats <5fl	6.0 (15)	0.3 (7)	3.0 (38)	5.2
Flats >4fl	0.7 (1)	0.0	0 (0)	0.0
Maisonette	1.0 (1)	0	0.7 (6)	0.0
	39.7(100)	13.3(100)	8.7(100)	38.3

Table 4   *Breakdown of passive systems by type of dwelling*

Age categories	Conservatory %	Roof collector %	Trombe wall %	No side to south %
Pre-1900	5.0 (12)	4.0 (29)	1.0 (9)	9.0
1900 to 1918	3.0 (7)	1.0 (10)	0.0 (3)	7.0
1919 to 1939	11.5 (29)	5.0 (40)	1.7 (21)	7.8
1940 to 1950	2.7 (8)	1.0 (6)	1.0 (9)	3.3
1951 to 1969	11.5 (29)	1.3 (13)	4.0 (47)	8.2
Post-1970	6.0 (15)	1.0 (2)	1.0 (11)	3.0
	39.7(100)	13.3(100)	8.7(100)	38.3

Table 5   *Breakdown of passive systems by age group*

Sample = 413 dwellings
N.B. The figures in brackets represent the percentage breakdown within each passive system category.

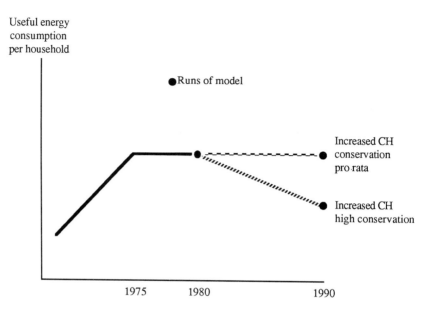

Figure 5   *High and low energy conservation scenarios (source: Leach and Pellew, 1982)*

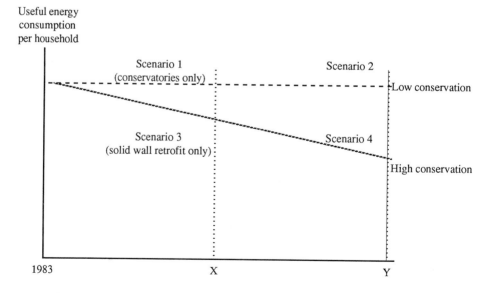

Figure 6   *The four basic passive solar scenarios*

fuel used for the domestic sector in the thirty year maximum time scale envisaged here. It would appear that gas (a mixture of natural gas and SNG) will, for a long time, provide most of the UK space heating fuel, supplemented by coal and to a lesser extent by electricity (Leach *et al.*, 1979).

Corresponding to the energy conservation hypothesis as shown in Figure 5, two main passive solar assumptions were made. In the first stage, only the houses with solid walls had passive solar systems fitted (if suitably orientated). It seemed logical, as a first step for a passive solar scenario, to consider houses with solid walls, since these are impractical and costly to insulate. In short, passive solar is considered as an 'alternative' to energy conservation.

In the second and more distant stage (Scenarios 2 and 4, at date Y in Figure 6), all the houses identified in the previous section as having a passive solar retrofit potential were taken into account. Scenarios 2 and 4 represent the maximum potential of the passive solar contribution in the existing housing stock following high and low energy conservation cases (both with 100% central heating).

Finally, the scenarios as expressed in Figure 6 were modelled for the entire stock. Separate scenarios were also applied to the private and the public sector, in order to evaluate the impact of passive solar according to the type of ownership.

Results

Conservatory scenarios

1) At the first stage X date (see Figure 7), it was found that 19% of the housing stock could accommodate a retrofit conservatory on to a solid wall house, which meant that most of the suitable cases were found among the private sector as the majority of the public sector belongs to the post-war period. In terms of performance this scenario would save between 5.4% and 6.5% (low and high cases) of the space heating load in the UK or around 1% of UK primary energy needs (1.1 mtoe).

2) At a later stage (date Y) all houses were considered for conservatory retrofits and account for a 39.7% potential of the entire stock. The number of conservatories roughly doubled compared to the previous stage but the savings did not because the solid

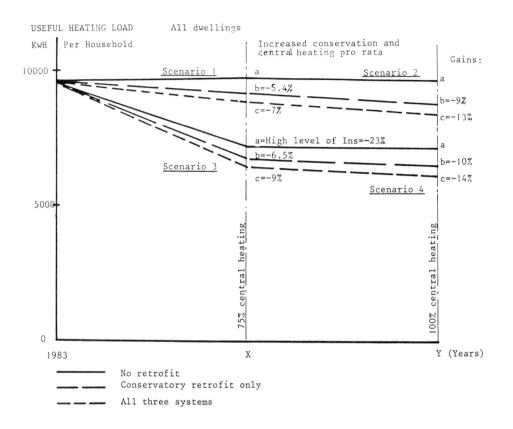

Figure 7   *Low and high energy conservation cases and passive solar scenarios*

Scenario 1
a = Increased conservation and central heating pro rata (no solar)

b = Conservatory retrofits for solid wall houses

c = Cons. + roof coll. + Trombe wall retrofits for solid wall houses

Scenario 3
b and c same as in Scenario 1 but applied to high level of insulation

Scenario 2
a = Increased conservation and central heating pro rata (no solar)

b = Conservatory retrofits for all suitable houses

c = Cons. + roof coll. + Trombe wall for all suitable houses

Scenario 4
b and c same as in Scenario 2 but applied to high level of insulation

wall/conservatory case concerned poorly insulated houses which gave better thermal performances. In total the savings would be 9% and 10% respectively of the domestic sector consumption for the low and high energy conservation cases which represents around 1.7% of UK primary energy requirements or 2.12 mtoe (low case).

Conservatory, roof collector and Trombe wall scenarios

1) The three systems combined at the first stage (solid wall retrofit only) yield a 27% retrofit potential in the entire existing housing stock, and are mostly concentrated in the private sector. Such a scenario would contribute between 7% and 9% savings (Scenario 1 and 3) for the domestic sector space heating load or 1.4% of UK primary energy needs (1.5 mtoe).

2) For the second stage all three systems combined represent the maximum potential for passive solar retrofit in the existing housing stock with 61.7% of the sample. This would contribute up to 13% of the UK domestic sector space heating load for the low energy conservation case, which is 2.28% of UK primary energy needs or 3.53 mtoe. For the high energy conservation case it would represent a 14% saving over the UK domestic sector space heating load or 2.45% of UK primary energy needs (3.80 mtoe).

Conclusion

It would seem that the most immediately realistic scenario is that which considers passive solar retrofits of solid walls only, for in these cases alternative methods for conserving energy would be inapplicable or ineffective. The savings which could be expected to accrue in this case alone are 9% for the domestic sector and 1.4% for total primary energy needs. Such passive solar retrofits could be applied to 27% of all dwellings.

On the whole, these figures seem to be of the same order of magnitude as the savings achievable through insulating all cavity walls in dwellings, assessed as between 2% and 2.5% of UK primary energy needs (Building Research Establishment, 1975). It has been suggested elsewhere (Leach and Pellew, 1982) that a vigorous energy conservation programme would save up to 17% of total UK domestic sector delivered energy or just under 5% of total UK primary energy needs. This conservation programme, combined with a maximum solar scenario, could save up to 7.5% of UK primary energy requirements or 30% of the domestic sector.

In conclusion, this analysis of the application of passive solar retrofits to the Cambridge housing stock suggests that the most significant role of such measures is in saving energy in houses with solid wall construction where no other options appear to be viable. In all the other cases investigated, the adoption of passive solar retrofits currently appears to be marginal. Nevertheless, wholesale application of all passive solar retrofits in all possible cases would still result in energy savings comparable to those expected from a programme of insulating all domestic cavity walls.

References

Building Research Establishment (1975). *Energy Conservation: a Study of Energy Consumption in Buildings and Possible Means of Saving Energy in Housing.* BRE Working Party Report, CP 56/75. Garston: BRE.

Leach, G. *et al.* (1979). *A Low Energy Strategy for the UK.* London: International Institute for Environment and Development.

Leach, G. (1981). *Energy-related Statistics for UK Dwellings.* London: International Institute for Environment and Development.

Leach, G. and Pellew, S. (1982). *Energy Conservation in Housing.* London: International Institute for Environment and Development.

Penz, F. (1983). *Passive Solar Heating in Existing Dwellings.* Report to the Energy Technology Support Unit, Harwell (Ref. ETSU S-1056a). The Martin Centre for Architectural and Urban Studies, University of Cambridge.

Penz, F. (1984). A graphical method to assess passive solar gains in the existing housing stock in the U.K. *Proceedings of the First E.C. Conference on Solar Heating.* Dordrecht, Holland: Reidel.

Uglow, C. (1981). The calculation of energy use in dwellings. *Building Services Engineering Research and Technology*, Vol. 2, No. 1.

ESTIMATING THE EXPOSED SURFACE AREA OF THE DOMESTIC STOCK

Philip Steadman and Frank Brown

Centre for Configurational Studies
The Open University

Abstract

This paper describes a general means for estimating the total area of exposed surface (walls and roofs) of a stock of domestic buildings, given data on floor areas and a specified mix of dwelling types. Empirical studies of a sample of house plans from the City of Cambridge, broadly representative of the British stock as a whole, show that strong regularities exist in the relation of exposed wall area to floor area, for different types of dwelling (mid-terrace, end-of-terrace, semi-detached, detached). Theoretical analysis of a range of idealized built forms shows how these regularities arise, as a result of the characteristic sizes of rooms in dwellings, the general requirement for daylighting and the constraints of close-packed rectangular geometry. Similar considerations apply to the aggregation of dwellings, i.e. terraces into rows, and flats into blocks.

The paper also considers the relation of roof area to floor area for different dwelling types, and the relation of glazed area to exposed wall area.

A sample of dwellings in Cambridge

The areas of exposed surface of a building (walls and roof) are important determinants of heat loss. The method used here for predicting the surface area of domestic buildings is based in the first place on the results of a programme of empirical analysis of the existing British housing stock. This work has made use of a random sample of dwellings in the City of Cambridge, selected originally for an investigation of the potential for passive solar heating, by the Martin Centre for Architectural and Urban Studies (Hawkes and Souza, 1981). That survey covered some 413 houses and flats, sampled from Electoral Registers. Subsequent statistical analysis has shown that the sample corresponds quite closely to the national housing stock as a whole in terms of date of construction, ownership and dwelling type (Penz, 1983; Brown and Steadman, 1985a).

The Martin Centre survey collected information about fabric, external geometric form, orientation and overshadowing of each dwelling, but it did not go into details of internal

113

plan arrangement. For the present work the same buildings were re-surveyed, and floor plans were obtained either from original drawings deposited in local archives or by making on-site surveys. Refusals by occupants to allow access meant that about 100 dwellings had to be discounted, reducing the final total to 305 sets of plans. Of these approximately 70% were obtained by on-site survey (Brown and Steadman, 1985b).

All these plans have been stored in a computer database to enable a whole series of measurements to be made automatically (Brown and Steadman, 1986). Plans are represented as sets of wall segments (straight lengths of exterior or partition wall running between junctions), recorded without thickness (Figure 1). Curved walls are approximated as sequences of short straight segments. In the case of an internal wall the line marks the centre-line of the partition. In the case of an external wall or a party wall the line denotes the outer face of the wall. Computed floor areas are therefore gross areas and must be adjusted by making suitable allowances for wall thicknesses, to obtain net area figures. Wall segments are coded according to type, either internal partition, party or external exposed walls. Floor-to-ceiling heights are also recorded, separately for each room if necessary.

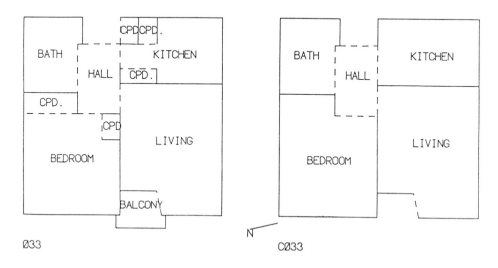

Figure 1   *A sample plan from the computer database of Cambridge house plans (C033 is a simplified version of plan 033)*

Enclosed spaces contiguous with the principal volume of the dwelling, such as conservatories and attached garages, are included in the computed floor, wall and roof areas. However, spaces which may be roofed but are otherwise open to the elements, such as porches and carports, are excluded; as are all balconies, terraces and loggias. No details of glazing areas or roof geometry are recorded. Data on these properties were, however, collected in the Martin Centre survey.

For each house or flat as a whole a number of identifying characteristics are recorded. These include the dwelling type in one of eight categories:

Mid-terrace
Terrace end
Semi-detached
Detached
Bungalow (i.e. single storey detached)
Flat in block of four storeys or less
Flat in block of five storeys or more
Maisonette (i.e. two storey-flat)

The age of dwelling in seven time-bands:

Pre-1850
1850-1899
1900-1918
1919-1939
1940-1963
1964-1969
1970-1981

The form of ownership:

Public housing
Housing association
Owner-occupied
Private rented

The on-site surveys involved making sketch plans, not measured drawings. Nevertheless, the recorded plans can be expected to be fairly accurate dimensionally. The external dimensions were obtained by measuring Ordnance Survey maps, and these and some internal dimensions were cross-checked by measuring photographs. In the larger houses some individual room areas may be inaccurate but these discrepancies should largely cancel out in the overall floor area figures. Plans derived from archive drawings will be dimensionally very accurate, although they may of course depart somewhat from the plans as actually built.

Exposed wall areas

Many types of measurement have been made of the dwellings in the sample; but among the most basic, and for the present discussion the most relevant, are measurements of (gross) floor area, F, and measurements of total exposed exterior wall area EW, (the latter *including* the areas of windows and doors).

Figure 2 shows the ratio of these quantities EW/F for some of the dwelling types in the sample. The distribution of this ratio for mid-terrace houses is strongly peaked around a modal value of 0.75. The distribution for semi-detached and end-terrace houses taken together is peaked around 1.05. The distribution for detached houses and bungalows taken together is flatter, and peaks around 1.15.

Why should these results arise? It is not difficult to see that they have to do with the basic geometric forms of the different dwelling types. Certainly individual houses of the same general type will differ greatly in their detailed forms, with bay windows, back extensions, lean-to side additions and other articulations of plan and elevation. But at a more general and abstract level, we can characterize the underlying built forms of small dwellings as simple rectangular blocks with different numbers of sides exposed (Figure 3). In the detached house or bungalow all four sides are exposed. In the semi-detached or end-terrace house, three sides are exposed. In the mid-terrace house two (opposite) sides are exposed. These are of course the very properties by which the 'types' are distinguished in the first place.

These facts explain why we obtain characteristic and distinct modal values for the ratio of exposed wall area to floor area EW/F in each case. In detached houses, relatively more wall surface is exposed than in semi-detached, and in semi-detached relatively more wall is exposed than in terrace houses. But why do the ratios take the particular values which they do? For an explanation here we must look to the typical *dimensions* of dwellings.

The great majority of rooms in modern houses are daylit and lie on the exposed sides of the plan perimeter. The only general exceptions are circulation and storage rooms, and the

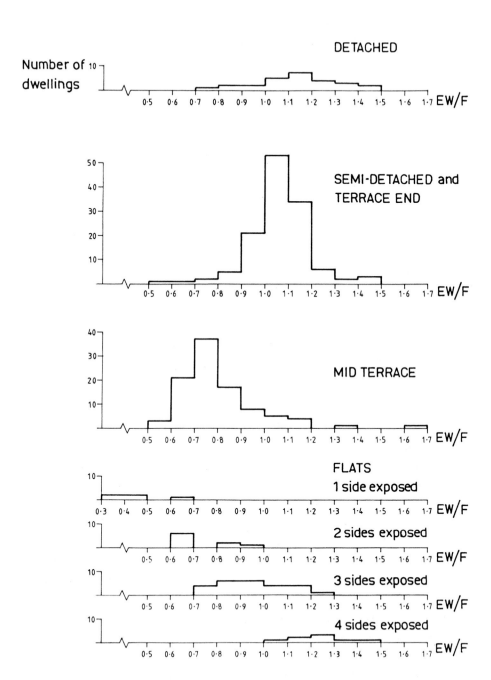

Figure 2   *Ratio of exposed wall area to floor area by dwelling type in the Cambridge sample*

Sides exposed

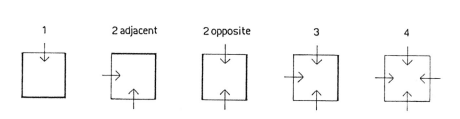

Figure 3   *The principal house types characterized as a series of built forms*

occasional bathroom. Analysis of the Cambridge sample shows that the mean value for the gross floor areas of 'living rooms' (living, parlour, dining, kitchen, study and various combinations thereof) is between 14 and 15 m^2, and for bedrooms between 13 and 14m^2. Obviously there is a large variance around these means. But just for the sake of diagrammatic illustration let us assume a typical 'habitable room' area of 14m^2. On the assumption that the room is square, this gives a typical room dimension of 3.75m.

Now let us consider in very schematic terms the internal organization of our terrace, semi-detached and detached 'built forms' (Figure 4). On the assumption that the plan in each case is at a maximum two 'habitable rooms' deep, each room taking its light from one exposed face of the building, we arrive at a total plan depth of 3.75 + 3.75 = 7.5m.

For the terrace form the frontage dimension x in Figure 4 is in principle indefinitely variable. In the semi-detached form the notional depth is again 7.5m. A strip along the exposed side wall of 3.75m width can be lit from this side. The frontage now becomes (3.75 + x) where x is again variable. Finally in the detached case, on a similar argument, the depth is 7.5m and the frontage (3.75 + 3.75 + x). The detached built form is shown here as a simple rectangle. Clearly however, where x is large, the resulting elongated block of accommodation might in practice be bent into L or T shapes, into branching wings and so on, while still preserving the same maximal depth throughout of approximately 7.5m.

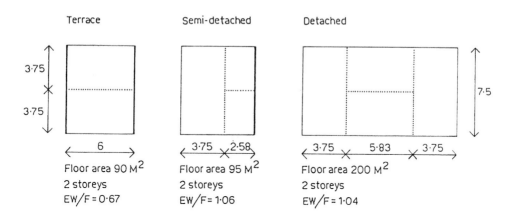

Figure 4   *Schematic representation of the internal layout of the three main house types*

It remains to determine typical values for the variable x in the expressions for frontage. These depend on the total area of accommodation provided, and the number of floors on which this is disposed. Figure 5 shows floor area F by type of dwelling in the Cambridge sample. In the case of terrace houses the distribution is strongly peaked around 90m^2. For semi-detached it is again strongly peaked, in this case around 95m^2. The distribution for detached houses and bungalows is, as might be expected, very flat, ranging from under 50m^2 to over 1000m^2.

Let us take the case of a typical terrace house on two floors (Figure 4). For a total floor area of 90m^2, this gives 45m^2 on each floor. It follows that frontage $x = 6$m. On the assumption of a storey height of 2.5m, the total exposed wall area is 30m^2, and the ratio EW/F = 0.67. Compare this with the value of 0.75 obtained in the survey of actual houses in Figure 2. The reason that the observed modal value is somewhat greater than the value from this theoretical calculation can be attributed to the fact that many terrace houses, especially those with frontages less than 6m, increase their exposed wall area somewhat, relative to floor area, by the device of the back extension, containing typically a kitchen or scullery below and a bedroom or bathroom above.

For the case of the typical semi-detached house, on a similar argument, we have a total floor area of 95m^2, disposed on two floors of 47.5m^2 each (Figure 4). This gives a frontage of 6.33m, i.e. $x = 2.58$. Again assuming a storey height of 2.5m, then the total

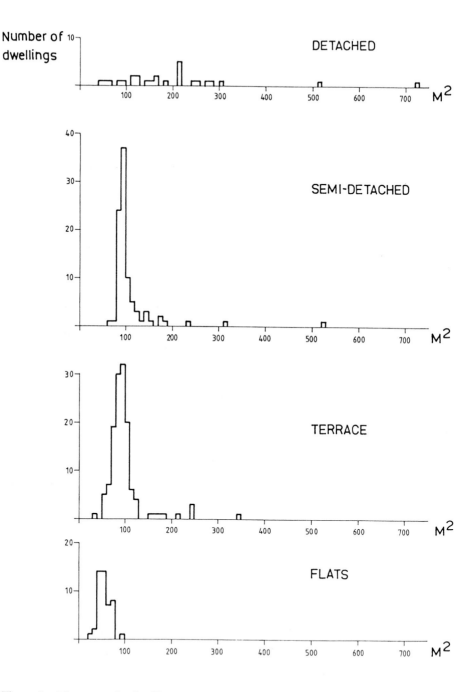

Figure 5   *Floor area by dwelling type in the Cambridge sample*

exposed wall area = 100.8, and the ratio EW/F = 1.06. This is very close to the modal value observed in the Cambridge sample as in Figure 2. (It is a curious fact, of no very profound significance, that in many classic semi-detached houses of the inter-war and immediate post-war periods, the exposed wall area is almost exactly equal to the floor area. Figure 6 shows a house of which the floor area, area of exposed external wall and total area of internal partition wall are all equal!)

Figure 6   *A standard form of semi-detached house, built by Cambridge Local Authority in the late 1940s and early 1950s*

For detached houses, as we saw earlier, there is wide variation in floor areas in the existing stock. If we select for the sake of illustration a house of $200m^2$ on two floors, this gives a frontage of 13.33m and a value for x of 5.83 (Figure 4). The exposed wall area is $208.3m^2$ for a storey height of 2.5m, and the ratio EW/F = 1.04. This is somewhat lower than the modal value of 1.15 for the actual sample as illustrated in Figure 2.

We are comparing here an isolated theoretical case with the peak of an empirically observed distribution. Nevertheless, it does appear that for detached houses the value of the ratio EW/F is generally higher in the existing stock than the foregoing line of argument would predict. One might expect *a priori* that room sizes in detached houses would be typically larger than in other dwelling types, and hence that building depths would be greater. This, however, would tend to reduce, not to raise the ratio of exposed wall to floor area, other things being equal. The truth seems to be the contrary, that the large sites on which detached houses are typically built allow for plans which, at least in part, are 'single pile' (only one room deep). Another factor is that the forms of detached dwellings tend to depart more widely than other types from simple rectangular blocks, and to be elaborated with many protrusions and extensions, which further tend to increase external wall area.

In general the distribution for values of EW/F in Figure 2 must reflect similar variations in building depth, in the complication of external form by projections and additions, and other factors such as variations in storey heights and numbers of storeys. This theoretical demonstration has, however, shown that the relationships illustrated in Figure 2 are not mere fortuitous empirical regularities, but arise out of the basic nature of the rectangular geometry of houses, their typical room sizes and the demands of natural lighting. For these reasons it is plausible to expect that these kinds of relations will continue to hold for the housing stock in other British towns and cities, and indeed more broadly than that.

To go back briefly to the theoretical built forms in Figure 3: there should exist logically two more forms to complete the set; that in which two *adjacent* sides of the rectangular block are exposed, and that in which only one side is exposed. The latter corresponds to the notorious 'back-to-back' houses built in some Northern industrial cities in England in the 1870s and 1880s (and now being reintroduced in some private developments in the 1980s). The type with two adjacent sides exposed is rarer; but this too is found in the same region at the same period. Figure 7 shows such houses, grouped in blocks of four, built in Keighley, Yorkshire, *circa* 1885.

From the point of view of any analysis of the present stock these types are largely irrelevant, since they have all but disappeared. It is still of some theoretical interest to look at the ratio EW/F in these houses, for the sake of completeness. The house with two adjacent sides in Keighley has a value for the ratio of 0.53. (Compare this with the modal value for terrace houses in Figure 2 of 0.75.) A small sample of five true back-to-backs with only one side exposed in each case, drawn from Muthesius (1982), gives values for the ratio between 0.29 and 0.67, with a mean of 0.45. In some cases, including the

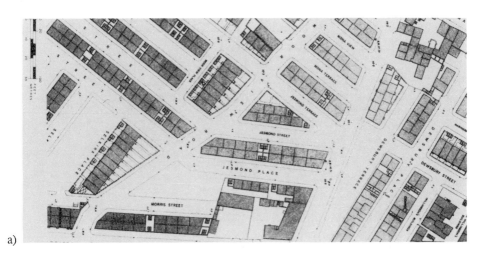

a)

Figure 7

a) *An area of back-to-back houses
    in Leeds*

b) *A cut-away view of a typical
    'back-to-back'*

c) *A grouping of four 'back-to-
    backs' in Second Avenue,
    Keighley, Yorkshire*

(source: Muthesius 1982)

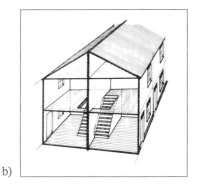

b)

c)

Keighley house, the value of the ratio is very low because accommodation is provided in cellars and attics (with no exposed wall area).

A type which *is* found extensively in the contemporary stock and which we have not yet covered is the flat. From the analysis of the Cambridge sample we have statistics on floor area and wall area for individual flats, although we have no measurements of the overall properties of the blocks in which these units are found. It is possible to characterize the basic plans of flats in terms of a range of built forms which are directly analogous to those for houses (Figure 3).

Thus rectangular flats can be aggregated into blocks in such a way that individual flats have either one, two, three or four sides exposed. It might be thought that the type with four exposed sides is rather rare. However, this occurs in a number of cases in the Cambridge sample, for example in ground floor flats with an open passage through the block at ground level.

Figure 2 shows the ratio EW/F for the small number of flats in the Cambridge survey. The diagram distinguishes flats with one, two, three and four exposed sides. (In the case of two exposed sides, these are all flats of a 'terrace' type, with two opposite sides exposed.) These distributions centre roughly around values of 0.5, 0.75, 1.0 and 1.25 respectively.

Figure 5 shows that the modal floor area for flats in the Cambridge area is $50m^2$. On arguments similar to those made for houses earlier, this means that the frontage dimension for flats takes a value of 13.33 for one exposed side and a value of 6.67 for two opposite, three and four exposed sides. Assuming a storey height of 2.5m, this gives values for the ratio EW/F of 0.67, 0.67, 1.04 and 1.42 for one, two, three and four walls exposed (compare Figure 2).

In the case of one side exposed, these calculations assume a depth for the flat of 3.75m. In practice it seems that greater depths are accepted for flats of this type, perhaps with internal bathrooms or kitchenettes; and that as a result the ratio EW/F drops, as Figure 2 confirms (although for five cases only).

Roof areas

So far we have examined only wall areas. Measurements have also been made of roof areas for the Cambridge sample. These relate however to roof *plan* areas, not to areas of sloping surfaces. The calculations measure in effect the ceiling area of the top storey of the house in each case. The plan areas of roofs of any extensions are also included, but roofs of porches, bay windows and other small projections are omitted. For houses with attic storeys or attic conversions, only the flat ceiling area is counted and not the sloping parts of the roof which form the 'walls' of the attics.

These figures do not therefore allow us to make a complete calculation of the true exposed surface area of each dwelling (except in the case of houses with flat roofs). They do, however, correspond more closely to those areas within the roof which are normally insulated, or capable of being insulated, and thus are arguably of greater interest from the point of view of heat loss.

The Martin Centre survey collected information about roof geometry which could in principle be used to compute areas of sloping surfaces for pitched roofs, although this has not yet been done.

Ratios of roof area R, on this definition, to floor area F are shown in Figure 8 for detached, semi-detached plus terrace-end and mid-terrace houses, as before. The ratio R/F is determined in effect simply by the number of floors on which the accommodation is disposed. Thus, not surprisingly, the distributions are strongly peaked around 0.5 in all cases, marking the great preponderance of two-storey dwellings in all three categories. The ratio rises somewhat above 0.5 for two-storey houses with single-storey extensions, and falls slightly below 0.5 for two-storey houses with bay windows and other similar features which add to floor areas without increasing computed roof area. Bungalows appear with an R/F value close to 1, and houses on numbers of floors greater than two with fractional R/F values appropriate to these numbers of storeys.

Putting statistics for exposed wall area EW together with those for roof area R, we can obtain ratios for total exposed area to floor area (EW + R)/F, as illustrated in Figure 9. In the case of detached houses, low values for this ratio correspond in general to larger houses, of greater average depth, with simple and compact plan forms. Meanwhile higher values correspond to smaller houses, with more elaborated plan forms, in some cases only

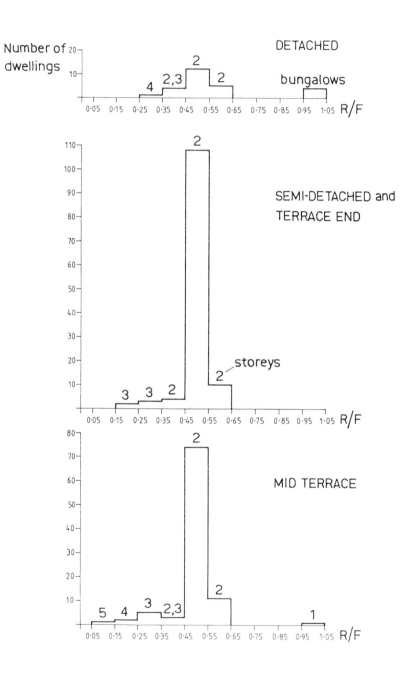

Figure 8   *Ratio of (flat) roof area to floor area by dwelling type in the Cambridge sample*

one room deep. Another factor, clearly, is the number of storeys. In general the size of detached houses is such that, built on two floors, their forms are a long way from the cube. Putting the same accommodation on three or more floors reduces the total surface area, and so reduces the value of the ratio (EW + R)/F. Similar factors are at work in the distributions for semi-detached and terrace houses.

Glazing areas

One further property of exposed surface area which is of interest from the point of view of heat loss is the area devoted to glazing. Recall that the exposed wall area EW as calculated here includes all windows and doors. Broad estimates of glazed areas for the

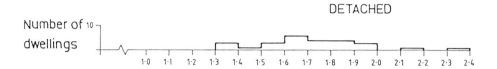

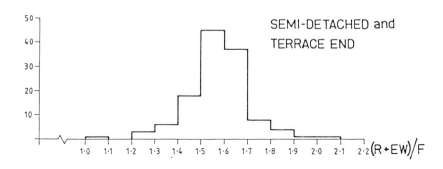

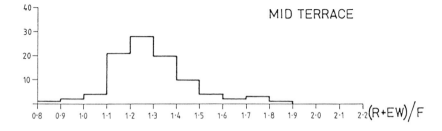

Figure 9 *Ratio of total exposed surface area to floor area by dwelling type in the Cambridge sample*

Cambridge sample were made by the Martin Centre. But the Martin Centre's interest was focused principally on south-facing glazing, and total areas of windows were extrapolated from measurements made for one or two walls of each house only. For the present purposes some precise measurements have been made, for a small selection of representative house types. The results are suggestive of certain relationships, although more work is needed to examine these properties on a statistically meaningful basis.

It might be expected *a priori* that, as the area of exposed wall is decreased in relation to floor area, from detached to semi-detached to terrace houses, so the proportion of that wall area devoted to glazing would increase. To put it another way, the same area of window needed to light a fixed area of floor would become concentrated into progressively smaller areas of exposed wall. In practice this does not seem to be the case, or not to any marked extent. The table below shows glazing area as a percentage of exposed wall area for six selected houses.

		%
1.	Small narrow-frontage terrace	14.5
2.	Wider frontage terrace without bay window	14.5
3.	Wider frontage terrace with bay window	19.0
4.	Private inter-war semi-detached	19.9
5.	Large Victorian semi-detached	15.5
6.	Modern detached	13.7

Tentatively we might conclude that the total area of glazing is determined by the need to supply *some* light to all principal rooms, rather than being related directly to lighting levels as such. Other factors such as construction technology (as it affects widths of openings) and fashion (such as that for 'picture windows' in the 1960s) clearly also come into play. It seems plausible that with measurements from a larger sample it would be possible to predict glazing area on the basis of type and age of dwelling and exposed wall area. (Extensions, especially added conservatories might, however, need special consideration.)

Conclusion

Suppose then that it is required to predict the exposed surface area of a stock of domestic buildings for some part of Britain say, other than Cambridge, on the basis of data on total floor area broken down by dwelling types. In essence the proposal is that the distribution for the ratio R/F in Figure 8 be used to predict (flat) roof areas; the distributions for the ratio EW/F in Figure 2 be used to predict exposed wall areas; and a ratio G/EW derived from further empirical work be used to predict glazing areas on the basis of exposed wall areas.

The problems arising are of two kinds. First there is the problem of how representative the Cambridge stock is of the national stock as a whole, and whether regional or local variations in house types might not bring about changes in the relationships illustrated in Figures 2 and 8. The second problem is that of the aggregation of dwellings into larger groups or blocks.

We will not dwell at length on either of these problems, which are the subject of continuing research, but will just make some general comments here. On the matter of the representativeness of the Cambridge sample, reference has already been made to comparisons of the Cambridge results with national statistics. Cambridge houses are generally somewhat larger in terms of floor area (and hence also wall and roof area) than national averages for equivalent types, especially in the detached category (Penz, 1983). This reflects a general trend for houses in the south of the country to be larger than those in the north. There are also large differences between Cambridge and national statistics in numbers of detached houses as a percentage of all types, detached houses being under-represented in the Cambridge results. This can be attributed mainly to the fact that the Cambridge survey took an urban sample and did not cover rural areas in which higher proportions of detached houses are to be found. The percentage of all dwellings represented by flats in Cambridge is similar to the national picture, but clearly this percentage would rise substantially for London and other metropolitan areas.

None of these discrepancies presents serious difficulties for the proposed method of estimation, so long as local data on floor areas and the breakdown of dwelling types are available. There are likely to be significant variations in typical internal room arrangements in houses between different parts of the country, reflecting regional vernacular traditions and the influence of local authority housing departments, but these too should not in themselves cause problems in predicting surface areas, for the reasons argued earlier. More problematic, potentially, is the possibility that these plan differences may be associated with regional and local differences in the typical numbers of storeys for different dwelling types; since these will significantly affect the relationship of floor area to surface area, especially roof area, as we have seen.

The question of the aggregation of dwellings into groups also needs more study. For detached houses the issue does not of course arise, and for semi-detached it is unproblematic. But for terrace houses the ratio of mid-terrace to terrace-end is determined by the average length of terraces. And in order to compute surface areas for blocks of flats as a whole it will be necessary, besides floor area data, to have data both on numbers of storeys and on the distribution of different generic plan configurations, in which one-, two-, three- or four-sided flats (compare Figure 3) are packed together in different numbers and arrangements on each floor.

Some preliminary work on Ordnance Survey maps of Cambridge shows that the average terrace length in the city as a whole is 6.1 houses; and that this varies between averages of 9 or 10 in the medieval centre and in the 19th century 'bye-law' developments immediately surrounding the centre, down to average lengths of 4 or 5 houses in the outer suburbs. These spatial differences correspond clearly to differences in the average age of dwellings, with a consistent trend towards shorter terraces observable from the oldest developments to the newest. There is one slight complication in relating these terrace lengths taken from maps to the consequent proportions in the stock of mid-terrace and end-terrace houses; and that is, in the older terraces especially, that end-terrace properties are often devoted to commercial uses, such as pubs and 'corner shops'.

References

Brown, F.E. and Steadman, J.P. (1985a). *Housing in Cambridge: a Computerised Catalogue of a Sample of British House Plans, I: Background and Introduction.* Research Report. Centre for Configurational Studies, The Open University.

Brown, F.E. and Steadman, J.P. (1985b). *Housing in Cambridge: a Computerised Catalogue of a Sample of British House Plans, II: House Plans.* Research Report. Centre for Configurational Studies, The Open University.

Brown, F.E. and Steadman, J.P. (1986). A computerised database of contemporary house plans. *Planning and Design*, Vol. 13, No. 4.

Hawkes, D. and Souza, C. (1981). *Passive Solar Heating in Existing Housing: a Survey of the Housing Stock of Cambridge.* The Martin Centre for Architectural and Urban Studies, University of Cambridge.

Muthesius, S. (1982). *The English Terraced House.* New Haven and London: Yale University Press.

Penz, F. (1983). *Passive Solar Heating in Existing Dwellings.* Report to the Energy Technology Support Unit, Harwell (Ref. ETSU S-1056a). The Martin Centre for Architectural and Urban Studies, University of Cambridge.

THERMAL EFFICIENCY OF BUILDING CLUSTERS: AN INDEX FOR NON AIR-CONDITIONED BUILDINGS IN HOT CLIMATES

Vinod Gupta

School of Planning and Architecture
New Delhi, India

Abstract

The thermal behaviour of common building forms is well known but this behaviour is altered when buildings are laid out in clusters. The overall building form, the extent of glazed and unglazed surface area, the building orientation and the proximity of other buildings determine solar heat gains to the building. A geometrical property of the building called solar exposure can be used to determine relative efficiency of different types of building clusters in both warm and cold climates. For air-conditioned and/or heated buildings the solar exposure bears a direct relationship to the energy used for heating and air-conditioning, but no such relationship exists between thermal discomfort (or comfort) obtained in non air-conditioned buildings in warm climates and the building solar exposure. However, it is found that solar exposure per unit surface area of building is related to the discomfort index and the former is therefore a good indicator of the relative thermal performance of buildings in different urban layouts. Extended building forms with large external surface areas are useful in hot climates, but even better results can be obtained when compact forms are used with highly articulated surfaces.

Introduction

It is well known that thermal interaction between the internal environment of a building and the ambient conditions takes place through the building envelope. Since it is important to exclude unwelcome climatic extremes from buildings, the principles of good thermal design for temperate climates require:

1)   a building that promotes solar heat gain,

2)   a low surface to volume ratio to reduce conductive heat flow, and

3)   a tight building envelope to reduce infiltration.

133

Correspondingly, for hot arid climates, thermal design principles call for:

1)   a building form that intercepts least possible solar radiation,

2)   a low surface area to volume ratio, and

3)   a building design that promotes ventilation when needed.

In an earlier paper (Gupta, 1984b), a method for comparing the solar efficiency of archetypal building clusters called pavilion, court and street, was presented. The method used to determine relative efficiency was similar to that used by Knowles (1974), and it depended upon the calculation of 'solar exposure', a quantity which takes into account the area of irradiated surfaces of buildings as well as the variations in intensity of direct and diffuse solar radiation incident on each surface in the building cluster.

Taking a large building volume, a number of possible combinations of building clusters were analysed for solar exposure. These building forms had different external wall and roof areas, building depths and dimensions of internal partitions, while the window area taken as a fixed percentage of the floor area was equal in all the different forms. Solar heat gains to the building take place through the building fabric and through the windows. The actual heat gain to the building interior is reduced by the thermal resistance and thermal capacity of the envelope and by shades used over windows. Solar exposure would provide a good indication of the possible heat gains if the building was poorly insulated, had very lightweight external walls and roof or if it had large windows. For buildings with slightly better construction, it has yet to be seen if solar exposure is the critical factor that governs internal temperatures and potential energy expenditure.

In developing countries with a hot arid climate, yet another factor needs to be taken into account. Even though air-conditioning might be considered a necessity in these countries, it is normally not affordable and most buildings rely upon other methods for providing thermal comfort. The thermal behaviour of these non air-conditioned buildings is quite different from that of air-conditioned buildings as heat flows into the building during daytime while it flows out at night. The design principles for such buildings may have to be quite different from those for air-conditioned buildings.

Thermal analysis

Broadly speaking, there are two methods of predicting temperatures within buildings: (1) steady-state analysis, and (2) time-dependent analysis. The former can at best give very approximate results with respect to temperature variations and is therefore useful only for heated buildings in temperate climates, while the latter takes into account heat storage effects associated with massive structures that are typical of hot regions. This can take various forms such as finite difference method, Fourier transform technique, response-factor method and the admittance procedure.

Although the theory is well developed for each of these procedures, their accuracy in practice is limited by the unavailability of accurate data for important parameters like heat transfer co-efficients, infiltration rates and even thermal conductivity. In the present context these parameters may not pose such a problem as they would affect the different forms in a similar manner. More important will be the variations in the pattern of sunlight and shade that occurs over the façades of buildings in a cluster (Figure 1). To account for such variations it is necessary to divide each building façade into a large number of small elements and to record and account for the diurnal lighting/shading pattern of each element separately. If the interaction between the different elements is considered, the calculations become very tedious and require a great deal of computer time.

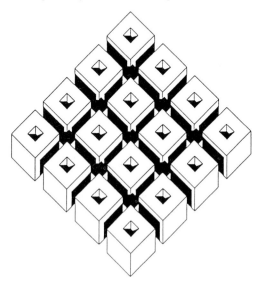

Figure 1   *Momentary light and shade pattern of a building cluster*

Keeping in mind these inherent limitations in predicting internal temperatures, building forms can be simplified for comparison of thermal performance without any further loss in accuracy. In this study, the following assumptions are made:

1)   Because of the difference in solar exposure, the thermal performance of blocks in a cluster will vary from the periphery where there is no shading, to the centre where there is shading. The average solar exposure of all the blocks is taken as the solar exposure of the typical block for the cluster. This condition is true for large clusters where edge effects are proportionately less.

2)   The envelope of each block is represented by four parts with distinct thermal inputs: (i) the roof, (ii) wall areas that are sunlit during daytime, (iii) wall areas that are shaded during daytime, (iv) windows.

3)   The variations in the relative proportion of sunlit and shaded wall areas are accounted for by adjusting the intensity of solar radiation while keeping the areas constant.

4)   The entire thermal mass of the building (internal floor and wall partitions) is separated from the building envelope so that heat flow between the envelope and thermal mass takes place mainly by convection and radiation.

5)   The space around the building, whether street or courtyard, is at a uniform temperature, even though it is known that in practice the courtyard temperature can be very different (Gupta, 1984a).

6)   Radiative heat loss to the sky from the walls is proportional to the area of sky 'seen' by the wall.

The computations of indoor temperatures were made by using an analytical model which considers the periodic heat flow through the four building elements defined earlier, while the floor of the building is taken as a semi-infinite medium. The model ignores the effect of vapour pressure, and its output is the time-dependent temperature of the internal air.

Three building clusters (Figure 2), one each of pavilion, court and street types, have been evaluated. When choosing the physical configuration the total volume of the cluster was taken as 800,000 m^3 corresponding to 266,666 m^2 of floor area, the height of all buildings as 12m and the depth of building blocks approximately 10m. The distance between building blocks is half the height of the buildings. The physical and solar properties of the three clusters are given in Table 1. Further it is assumed that the external walls are made of 25cm thick brick and the roof is 25cm thick concrete. Internal walls which occur at every 5m distance are 12cm thick and the intermediate floors are also 12cm thick. These building specifications are commonly used in India. The following analysis was carried out with temperatures and solar data for a hot summer day in New Delhi.

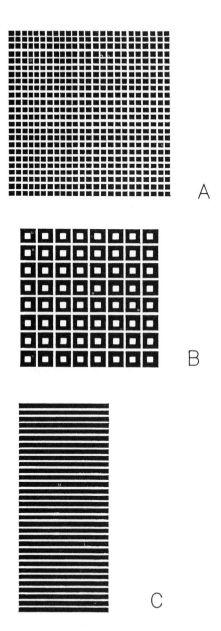

Figure 2   *Three possible configurations of a given building volume of 800,000 m³:*
(A) pavilion, (B) court, (C) street. The first two are possible housing
layouts, while the third represents institutional or commercial buildings.

		Pavilion	**Court**	**Street**
Physical properties				
(a)	Number of blocks in the cluster	576	64	32
(b)	Height (m)	12	12	12
(c)	Width of block (m)	10.76	10	10
(d)	Length of block (m)	10.76	36.04	208.33
(e)	Roof area (m^2)	66,668	66,668	66,668
(f)	External wall area (m^2)	297,435	160,000	172,916
(g)	Total external surface area (m^2)	364,103	226,668	239,584
(h)	Surface area/volume	0.45	0.28	0.30
(i)	Internal partition area (m^2)	697,437	867,202	867,200
(j)	Window area (m^2)	40,000	40,000	40,000
(k)	Volume of buildings (m^3)	800,000	800,000	800,000
Solar properties				
(a)	Daily total summer solar exposure (m^2)	586,709	493,364	437,488
(b)	Solar exposure/surface area	1.611	2.177	1.826
(c)	Equivalent radiative loss area (with 6m street width) (m^2)	123,180	100,268	101,251

Table 1   *Physical and solar properties of three configurations of a given building volume*

Thermal comfort index

The internal air temperatures obtained from this analysis are shown in Figure 3. These are shown under three conditions: (a) when there is no shading of windows and no ventilation in the building, (b) when 95% of window area is shaded and (c) when 95% of window area is shaded and the building is continuously ventilated with 6 air changes per hour. Since the temperatures show considerable fluctuation over the 24 hour period it is difficult to make a simple comparison, but it can be seen that the amplitude of temperatures is greatest for the pavilion and much less for the court and street. For a more accurate assessment of the energy required to bring the temperatures within comfortable limits,

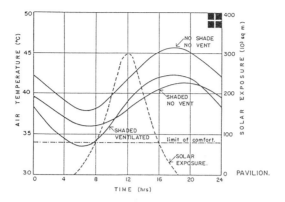

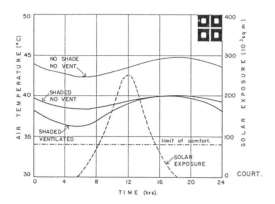

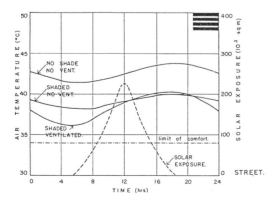

Figure 3   *Air temperatures and solar exposure for building clusters*

these have to be related to the human comfort range. Gupta and Spencer (1970) have suggested the use of a thermal discomfort index for unconditioned buildings where:

$$DISK = \frac{1}{N} \left[\Sigma_{day \atop hours} \left\{ \frac{T_{ia} - T_c}{\Delta D} \right\}^+ + \Sigma_{night \atop hours} \left\{ \frac{T_{ia} - T_{un}}{\Delta D} \right\} \right]$$

Where DISK = degree of discomfort

N = number of ordinates considered in a design cycle

T_{ia} = temperature of internal air space, °C

T_c = daytime preferred temperature, °C

T_{un} = upper limit for night-time comfort, °C

ΔD = deviation allowed in the daytime (half the range of comfort zone °C)

ΔN = variation allowed in night-time, °C

+   = only positive values to be considered, negative ignored

Because hourly temperatures are related to a preferred temperature, this index provides a good basis for comparison of building thermal performance. Since the summer temperature in non air-conditioned buildings does not go below the comfort range, the discomfort index can be modified to:

$$DISK = \frac{1}{N} \left[\Sigma_{24\ hours} \{T_{ia} - T_{uc}\}^+ \right]$$

Where T_{uc} is the upper limit of comfortable temperatures.

(The preferred summer temperature for Indian conditions is given as 27.5 ± 2.5°C at 50% relative humidity. For non air-conditioned buildings the upper limit of thermal comfort is taken as 34°C which is considered only moderately warm (Sharma, 1977).

Building performance index

The discomfort indices so obtained for the three different conditions have been plotted against solar exposure in Figure 4. In each case it is seen that although the pavilion form has the highest solar exposure it has the lowest DISK value and the court form has the highest DISK value even though its solar exposure lies somewhere between the street and the pavilion. Furthermore, if the surface area of the pavilion is increased without changing its solar exposure - a condition which corresponds to articulation of the external surface (Figure 5) without changing the overall form - the DISK value is lower still. Clearly, solar exposure by itself is not an indicator of the thermal efficiency of a building form in a warm climate. There are other more influential factors which control the internal air temperatures.

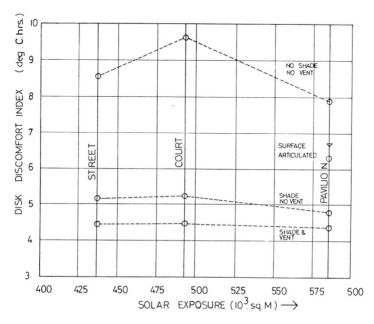

Figure 4   *Discomfort index as a function of solar exposure*

As already noted, the three building configurations have many common features including volume, floor area, roof area and window area. The main difference lies in the extent of the external wall area. External surfaces transmit heat into the building, but in a warm climate these surfaces lose heat to the exterior as well. The usefulness of a particular arrangement of surfaces in a building depends upon the relative efficiency of these in allowing heat into and out of the building. In our case one can say that outward heat flow occurs through all the external surfaces and is therefore proportional to the area of these surfaces. Radiative heat gain, on the other hand, depends upon the solar exposure which is a measure of the area of the building exposed to the sun. Thus the efficiency of the building envelope can be related to the solar exposure per unit external surface area of the building. Figure 6 shows the DISK values for the three forms, plotted against solar exposure/surface area (SE/SA). There appears to be an almost linear relationship between

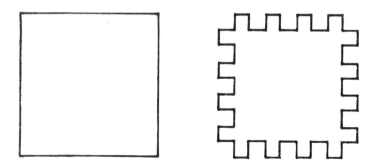

Figure 5   *Surface area increase by articulation of building envelope*

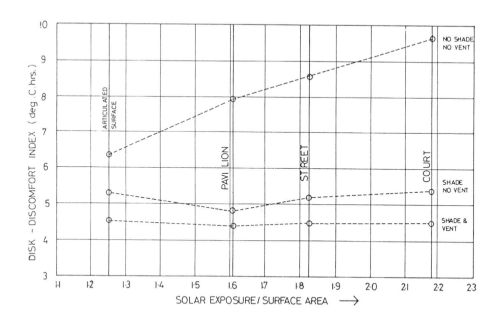

Figure 6 *Discomfort index as a function of solar exposure per unit surface area*

DISK and SE/SA including the case of the articulated pavilion. Since solar exposure has the same units as surface area, we have here a non-dimensional indicator of the thermal performance of a building form for a hot climate. Knowles (1974) has used a similar indicator for a cold climate with the difference that a bigger SE/SA value means greater efficiency there.

The relative surface area and solar exposure properties of urban built forms were reported by Gupta (1984b), from which it is possible to choose forms with a particular range of surface area per unit volume, and to choose forms with a particular range of solar exposures. But it is a much more complicated and difficult task to choose a form with a low solar exposure per unit surface area. As we have already seen, the court form with a low solar exposure performed badly because it had a low surface area as well. Its solar exposure per unit surface area was the highest.

One could therefore begin with a form with a large surface area and see if it is possible to limit its solar exposure by re-arranging it, by changing its orientation and by decreasing the distance between buildings. A more fruitful and easier approach, however, is to choose a built form with low solar exposure and to try to increase its surface area. This is achieved easily by surface articulation and by perforations in the building mass.

This in fact the method used in Jaisalmer, a medieval town in the Thar Desert in India. The overall built form of Jaisalmer has many shared walls and therefore rather low solar exposure (Figure 7). The building mass is broken up by courtyards and the overall building surface has many projections in the form of balconies and sunshades. But what is really remarkable is the articulation of the building surface itself. The entire stone façade of the Jaisalmer house is intricately carved, creating small fins which increase the surface area many times (Figure 8). It is not a mere coincidence that the thermal performance of these buildings is remarkably good (Gupta, 1985).

Conclusion

It has been demonstrated that solar exposure by itself is not a good index of the efficiency of a building form in a hot climate and that other building features can nullify the effect of solar exposure. In view of the fact that massive building elements such as brick walls and concrete roofs moderate solar heat gains even in cold climates, the applicability of solar exposure as a measure of building efficiency is doubtful even here. However, if one

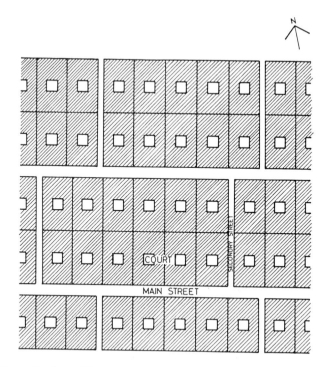

Figure 7   *Schematic plan of Jaisalmer town*

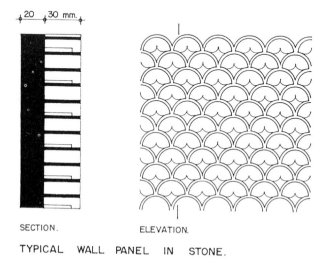

Figure 8   *Detail of building façade of a Jaisalmer house*

could have two building forms equal or nearly equal in all respects except for solar exposure, the choice between them could be based upon solar exposure.

Acknowledgements

The author gratefully acknowledges the help of Ashwini Kumar and Sant Ram of the Indian Institute of Technology, New Delhi, Srimoy Basu of the School of Planning and Architecture, New Delhi, and Peter Rickaby of The Open University, Milton Keynes, in the preparation of this paper.

References

Gupta, C.L. and Spencer, J.W. (1970). Building design for optimum thermal performance. *Australia Refrigeration, Air-Conditioning and Heating*. Nov. 1970, pp. 18-24.

Gupta, V.K. (1984a). Indigenous architecture and natural cooling. In *Energy and Habitat*, (Ed.) V. Gupta. New York: John Wiley, pp. 41-58.

Gupta, V.K. (1984b). Solar radiation and urban design for hot climates. *Environment and Planning B*, pp. 435-464.

Gupta, V.K. (1985). Natural cooling systems of Jaisalmer. *Architectural Science Review*, Vol. 28, No. 3, pp. 58-64.

Knowles, R. (1974). *Energy and Form: An Ecological Approach to Urban Growth*. Cambridge, Mass.: MIT Press.

Sharma, M.R. (1977). *Study of the Thermal Effects of Climate and Building on Human Comfort with Special Reference to India*. Doctoral dissertation, Agra University.

DESCRIPTION OF A COMPUTER TOOL FOR REPRESENTATION, MANIPULATION AND EVALUATION OF BUILT FORMS

Albert Dupagne, with Michael Renson

Laboratoire d'Etudes Méthodologiques Architecturales
Université de Liège, Belgium

Abstract

A computer program for interactive 3-D modelling of built forms is described as the centre-piece of a computer structure to be used for architectural design in an urban context. In this program, a building is seen as a collection of polyhedra (prism, pyramid, cylinder, ...) linked by a hierarchical set of relations. Polyhedra are created very simply by primitive commands, and geometric transformations can be applied on each polyhedron or on sets of volumes. Attributes can be attached to a volume's components (faces) or to the volume itself using catalogues through global commands as well as local exceptions (thermal physical data for walls, or desired comfort temperatures and occupancy parameters for spaces).

From the database, data files are produced allowing direct entry to various evaluation programs, i.e. heat-loss calculations, solar aperture and solar heat gains, direct incident solar energy on any face, shadowing and mask evaluation, and visual impact from different perspectives.

An example of an application is demonstrated on an urban space.

Introduction

An outstanding problem facing us at the present time is the difficult task of the rehabilitation of urban areas. This is particularly important in Europe for cultural and historical reasons, and has recently been emphasized by the European Commission through an exhibition devoted to the defence of European heritage.

The replacement of existing districts by entirely new large developments is no longer seen as an acceptable solution to the problem. Pulling down the existing buildings and starting again has proven to be detrimental to the townscape as well as to the inhabitants' way of life.

147

Urban renewal, especially in the context of an economic crisis, is more suited to the actual situation and to the application of limited resources. What is more, it is now considered an efficient and flexible process, easily adapted to differing situations. However, we must be aware that the renewal process is much more difficult to manage than simply rebuilding on a cleared site. Constraints of context are more stringent, for example, styles and cultural norms, but also the physical context in which each building operates. An existing building which is a candidate for retrofit must be considered separately with all its complex differentiation but also as part of an urban district with its own rigidity.

Surprisingly little work has been done on the development of efficient tools aimed to assist the renewal of the urban district as a whole. Probably this intermediate scale of action has been neglected because it is related both to urban planning and to architecture and consequently is not the specific province of either of the two professions. Urban built form is, however, the right scale at which to undertake action. As in architectural design, it is possible to modify details of the physical characteristics of existing buildings, and as in town planning, it is possible to take into account the reciprocal effect of any change on any part of the district considered. This approach preserves the general interest as well as the interest of the individual.

The CAM.UR research project

In mid-1985, a research proposal was submitted to the Commission of the European Communities for support. The aim of this project, called CAM.UR (Computer Aided Management system for Urban Renewal), is to produce a computer package to assist the passive retrofit and rehabilitation of existing cities throughout Europe.

The teams concerned were:

> LEMA, University of Liège, Belgium, Coordinator;
> ABACUS, University of Glasgow, United Kingdom;
> University of Dublin, Republic of Ireland;
> Synergia s.a., Bassano del Grappa, Italy;
> DIALOGIC s.a., Paris, France;
> Ethnoktimatiki s.a., Athens, Greece.

The proposal has now been accepted by the Commission as a Concerted Action project. It is based on results already obtained in Liège and this allows us to present the general concept of CAM.UR and the existing underlying computer structure.

The concept of the Intervention Unit (I.U.)

In order to make the best use of retrofit techniques, it is essential to take into account at the same time:

- the complex differentiation of each building, and
- the detailed nature of its specific environment.

Because of the large amount of data to be manipulated, an urban area cannot be considered as a whole, but must be subdivided into districts, each being made up of a limited number of blocks. A district is still too large to be manipulated easily and above all it is defined on an administrative basis which does not take account of the actual situation with real people living in real buildings and public open spaces. It is more concerned with zoning, planning and traffic management.

We therefore introduced the concept of the Intervention Unit (I.U.) as an actual living structure based on observations in the field and related to built forms, open spaces and inhabitants' behaviour. The Intervention Unit is, of course, a part of the district being studied: a street with adjacent buildings, a whole block, a square. This hierarchical breakdown of the urban area is carried out manually in order to produce the smallest part of the district which is significant at the urban level and self-sufficient.

This approach tries to be as realistic as possible. It supplies, in great detail, all geometric and physical features of forms and it reduces to the bare minimum the influence of transportation networks and other systems. These systems are more closely related to the town planning aspect and can be treated more efficiently at that level.

The Intervention Unit and the surrounding context

Each intervention on an existing urban space implies:

a) The precise definition of the geographical extent of the action

This has an important consequence. The whole urban space is then divided into two zones. The first one called the 'Intervention Unit' is the one concerned with the intended retrofit action. The second one is the rest of the urban space which is kept outside the Intervention Unit and not acted upon. Of course, it is important to limit the extent of the first zone in order to keep the work manageable. On the other hand, it is important to maintain in the controlled zone all parts of the urban context which have a perceptible effect on the Intervention Unit. There is an acceptable balance to find between a unit which is too large and inefficient and one which is too small and insignificant.

b) The definition of the specific environment of the I.U. according to the evaluations required

The environmental context of the I.U. is considered constant, at least during the time spent on the design of the intervention. Thus, the 'outer' environmental representation can be built at the beginning of the work and remain unchanged during the entire process.

The level of detail and the format required for the outer representation are determined by the evaluations of the Intervention Unit. Four different aspects have been identified and are shown in Figure 1.

1)   The topography is the shape of the ground on which the town has been built. It gives the geographical location of built forms and networks.

2)   The built forms are the set of building shapes. Together with the ground relief they permit the definition of solar masks. They also provide the context for visual impact evaluations.

3)   Networks are outside the scope of the retrofit action at the I.U. level. However, they have an important influence on the possible design alternatives and introduce some specific elements (like underground stations or bus stops) that are to be included in the I.U.

4)   Regulations and applicable norms introduce geometric and non-geometric constraints.

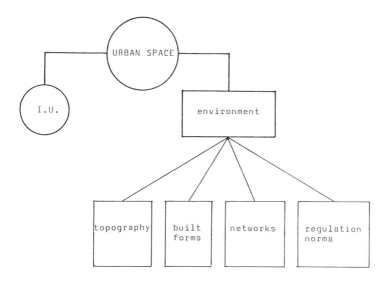

Figure 1   *Description of the Intervention Unit and its specific environment*

The structure of the Intervention Unit database

The 'inner' environmental representation of the Intervention Unit is described by three main sub-databases as illustrated in Figure 2:

1)   The volumes of plants
2)   The ground base
3)   The major built volumes

From these three databases we can build two reciprocal instances of the Intervention Unit, corresponding to the dual functional meanings of any urban space: the inner and outer spaces (Figure 2).

This distinction must be maintained throughout the entire design process because it reflects two essential aspects of human life: the individual and the collective consciousness. It is sustained by a set of reciprocal concepts illustrating its cultural and social importance such as: private-public, open-closed, in-out, individual-collective. Inner and outer spaces are inseparable concepts and the degree to which one complies with its own design goals depends directly on the way the other does. Very often, design goals in one problem

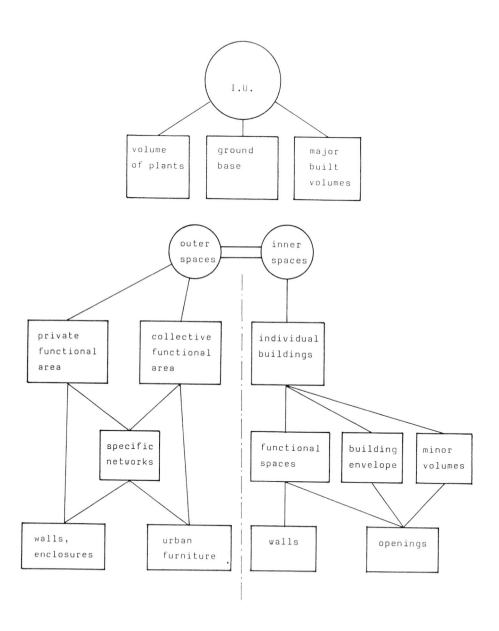

Figure 2   *The structure of the Intervention Unit database*

become constraints in the other. The global quality of the whole design depends on the balance reached between the two aspects. However, for purposes of clarity the two aspects are presented here in sequence.

The inner spaces

Urban architectural design is distinguished from sub-urban and rural architecture by two major characteristics:

1) Every design situation in an urban space is severely constrained. It is embedded in a very stringent context in which the building has to operate (such as the physical environment, regulations and norms or the socio-economic profile of the future occupants). The choice of the most appropriate design strategy is highly dependent on the particular situation.

2) The architectural significance of each building is difficult to consider in isolation. Of course, it has its own design goals and architectural logic, but it also receives an important part of its meaning from the global urban form in which it is found. It is part of another fabric at a high level of organization.

The consequence of these specific features is the necessity to perform evaluations of all kinds at the individual as well as the global level. No local optimum will be acceptable if a negative effect is induced in the global form. The I.U. representation in Figure 2 called 'inner spaces' gives the necessary information related to the evaluation of the global performances of the I.U. (visual, financial, energy, comfort, ...). In Figure 2, 'individual buildings' are linked to the 'inner spaces' database. This makes it possible to build the database required for the evaluation of the specific performance of one isolated building in the I.U. That is to say, the parameters describing the major built volume of the building in question are replaced or augmented in the 'inner spaces' database by the corresponding detailed features in the 'individual buildings' database.

The outer spaces

The design of urban built forms pays particular attention to the quality of open spaces. Of course they have a direct influence on the building's 'behaviour', and the way they are organized can permit or prevent some architectural functions in the surrounding buildings. But this particular attention is mainly due to the specific urban functions supported by public and private open spaces (such as gardens, markets, bus stops, playgrounds, squares). Each of these functions has its own requirements (surface area, volumes, temperature, wind velocity) and must be designed with the same careful attention often paid to the design of inner spaces. Because inner and outer spaces are closely linked in the hierarchical database (Figure 2), it is certain that any modification in one aspect is transferred to the other one in a consistent way.

Features of the urban renewal process

As is the case for any design process, urban renewal is based on a chain of cyclical sequences (analysis - synthesis - evaluation - decision) ending with the production of an acceptable solution. This very general model cannot explain some features of the urban renewal process we defined earlier. In particular, it does not take into account the existing situation and its inherent constraints on the definition of possible solutions. For example, the extent of the problem might be:

- to organize partial rehabilitation of a limited number of buildings;

- to replace some buildings but without alteration in plots and settlement;

- to rebuild the entire block.

Whatever the definition of the problem is, the knowledge of the existing situation is of major importance and must be available before solutions can be generated. A better representation of the design process can then be given. Figure 3 suggests an example of this.

However, this model is again too simple. It does not take into account the complex structure of interrelated concepts described above:

inner - outer spaces
global evaluation - simple evaluation

The chosen solution can be easily understood from Figure 2. If we consider first the upper level of the database and limit the evaluations to the inner and outer spaces, we can produce solutions applicable to the I.U. as a whole, as a global physical entity. These solutions try to reach an acceptable balance between inner and outer functional requirements. All the evaluations are performed on the whole unit and assess the global impact (visual, financial, energy, comfort) by using simple evaluation methods.

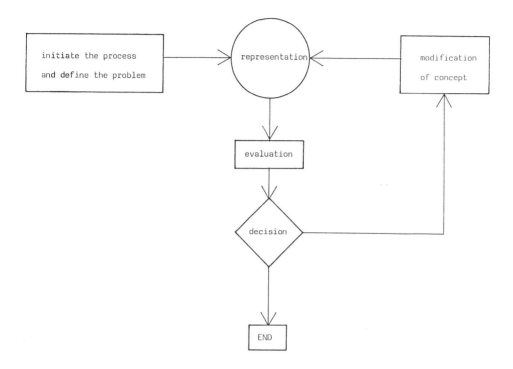

Figure 3   *Simple representation of the urban renewal process*

Once a global rehabilitation strategy or a set of possible retrofit actions have been defined, they are to be transferred to the local physical level of each element contained in the I.U. (individual buildings, public spaces, urban facilities). According to the quality of the data available at that level, detailed evaluations can be performed for each element in accordance with the boundaries already fixed at the upper level.

Description of the computer architecture of the program VOLUME

At the outset of its development, VOLUME was designed as a general computer structure allowing the easy preparation of the geometrical and physical data needed by the heating energy simulation program already at our disposal in the Laboratory. From the beginning we tried to keep VOLUME as general as possible. Then we gave it a modular structure and transferred to specific catalogues the data needed by the thermal evaluations. We therefore kept it open to many other evaluations as will be seen below.

Another feature of VOLUME, making it less specific than a simple building description language, is its object-oriented database structure allowing the set of 3-D volumes constituting the building to be stored. In VOLUME, a building is seen as a collection of elementary volumes representing spaces, each volume having its specific attributes appropriate to its characteristics and to the desired evaluation (e.g. architectural function, occupancy parameters). At a lower level, the faces of the volumes can be described precisely with openings and materials (Figure 4). All these geometric items are related by a hierarchical description: sets of volumes, volumes, faces, edges and vertices.

VOLUME also allows the modification of the database. It manages all the files and maintains the consistency of the data when the designer intervenes (by means of a range of simple commands) at each level of detail. For example, macro-commands are used to make global modifications on entire sets of volumes and, conversely, local actions and micro-commands permit vertices and edges to be moved. Any change made at any level is passed on to the other levels, and a check is made of the coherence between them.

Another point is the attention paid by VOLUME to the interface with the designer. It has been developed in order to facilitate the design or the modification of architectural forms. The designer has at his disposal a collection of polyhedra (prism, pyramid, cylinder, etc.) whose topology is already known by the program. He is able to give each of them a geometry by using simple commands and to manipulate them in order to produce any kind of built form he has in mind. According to our experience with practitioners, this way of working is easily understood by architects, especially at the beginning of the design process.

However, the 3-D structure can be considered as a first step, capable of modification during the design process towards a more detailed and complex one. The hierarchical database can be enriched easily at any level.

Figure 4 shows the way a building description is modelled in VOLUME. The first two columns contain the geometric characteristics of the building in a hierarchical structure. The Geometric Features column represents the kinds of data which are stored in the database files. In the two columns describing the physical features, the description of characteristics according to the nature of the item considered is often given a catalogue. For instance, the composition of a wall will only be described by a code number referring to the corresponding wall in a general catalogue.

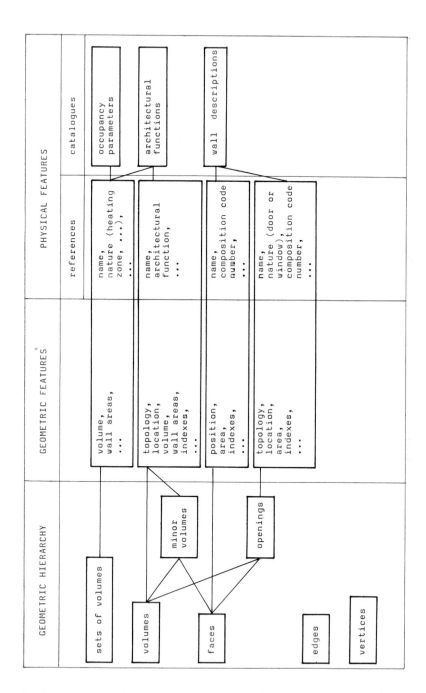

Figure 4   *Structure of the building description in VOLUME*

Because of its open structure there are no difficulties in extending the application of VOLUME to urban design problems. It has already been tried on a limited set of applications, presented below as an example. The main changes needed are the management of the large databases generated by urban design. They occur in the upper part of the geometric hierarchy (Figure 4), i.e in the different natures and attributes of simple volumes and faces. The lowest level, of course, remains unchanged. Major changes in computer hardware may make possible the management of such large databases in the future.

Evaluations

From the database built and managed by the program VOLUME, data files are produced by intermediate interfaces called 'data analysis programs' (Figure 5). Being developed in as general a way as possible, these modules can give access to a large set of evaluation programs. At the present time, three main data analysis programs have been implemented:

1)   VISTA, developed by the ABACUS Group at Strathclyde University, produces coloured perspective views with removal of hidden surfaces, and computation of shadow polygons.

2)   STEREO produces a stereographic spherical projection.

3)   GAM (Geometric Analysis Module) prepares the data needed for evaluations which require geometric parameters from the general database (adjacencies, surface areas, volumes, shortest paths, distances...).

The range of possible evaluations is large. Until now we have mainly concentrated our research effort on visual impact evaluation, solar analysis and thermal performance analysis, but we intend to increase the number and scope of evaluations in the foreseeable future.

Implemented evaluations include, for example:

DIRAD,   which is based on an hour-by-hour shadow polygon calculation and gives the direct incident solar energy received by any surface in the database in mean values for a day, a season or a year.

MASK,   which gives a stereographic projection of the shadow masks occurring at any point of the database.

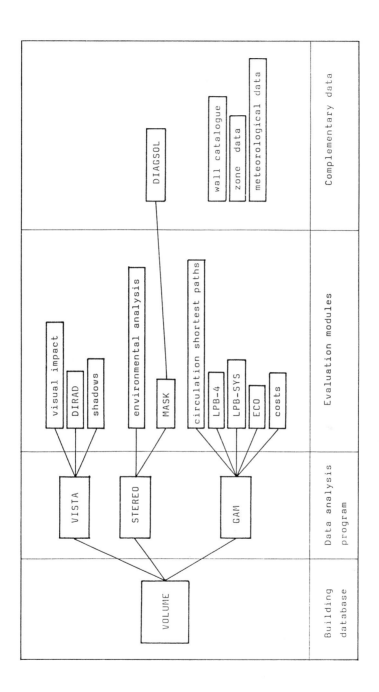

Figure 5 *Structure of the evaluation modules*

DIAGSOL,   which, in conjunction with MASK, calculates the sunshine periods in the year by superimposing a sun-path chart calculated for any latitude.

LPB-4,   which is a steady-state multizone simulation program which calculates the annual heating energy needs of a building.

LPB-SYS,   which calculates the annual fuel consumption of static heating equipment. It is a steady-state multizone program with dynamic corrections, in which the internal temperatures of the zones are parameters.

Application

In order to illustrate both the overall structure of the computer program and some of its features which are particularly well adapted to urban renewal practice, we would like to present some aspects of an actual problem we have recently been confronted with in a small town near Liège.

The application is concerned with the addition of a large extension to an existing building within a high-density suburban district. The neighbours contested this extension and tried to obtain evidence of the damage resulting to them. In order to make this clear and objective, they asked us to produce two demonstrations:

1)   A visual-impact analysis of the new building, which was intended to make evident its lack of integration with the surrounding district.

2)   A solar-impact analysis of the existing houses and open spaces (gardens, streets), with the objective of proving the resultant alteration in thermal comfort and heating energy needs.

In each analysis we decided to first compare the existing situation (Figure 6) with the one that would be created by the proposed extension (Figure 7). As will be demonstrated, this first comparison clearly illustrated the negative effects of the project, particularly with regard to its solar impact on the neighbours' houses.

But in Belgium town planning regulations do not consider the induced solar mask as a detriment to the neighbours, and their 'solar rights' are ignored. So we were unable to find a legal means to oppose the project. We decided then to demonstrate the existence of at least one alternative design for the building extension, satisfying both the owner's requirements and the constraints of the existing site (Figure 8). We hoped to bring all parties to an acceptable compromise.

According to the evaluations required we generated different databases with the help of the program VOLUME. Figure 9 illustrates the different levels of detail we adopted for the representation in relation to the possible evaluations made with each of them. It is important to note that certain evaluations required a specific combination of databases. The most detailed one consists of a complete description of the second project allowing us to perform a heating load evaluation. The last column on the right refers to the figure numbers where the results obtained are presented.

Acknowledgements

This paper is based on results produced by research projects sponsored by the Commission of the European Communities and the Services de la Programmation de la Politique Scientifique of the Belgian Government within the framework of their respective Research and Development Non-Nuclear Energy Programmes.

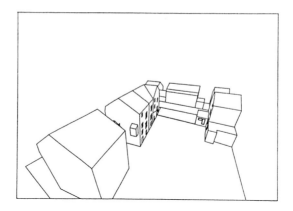

Figure 6   *Existing site: view from the north (database 12)*

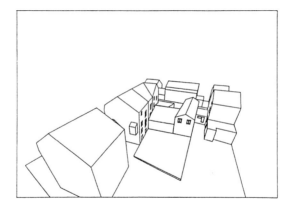

Figure 7   *Existing site plus first project (database 12 + 22)*

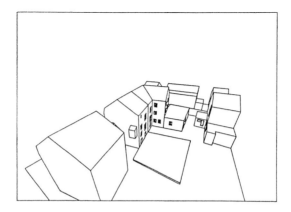

Figure 8   *Existing site plus second project (database 12 + 32)*

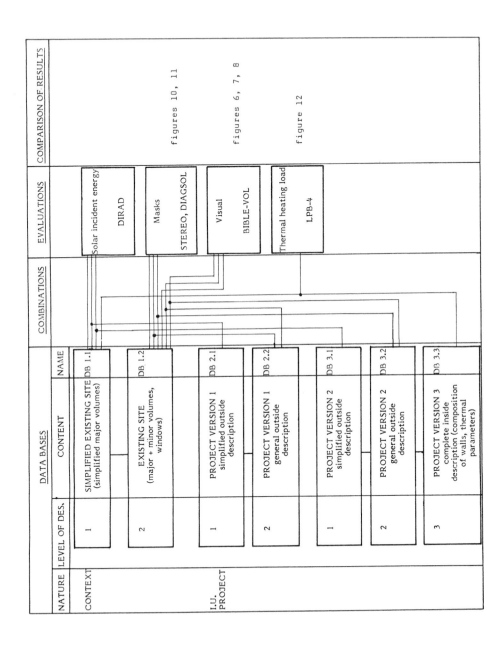

Figure 9   *Databases modelled*

Existing site

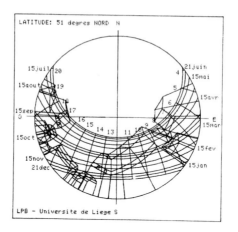

Project 1

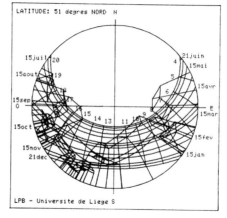

Project 2

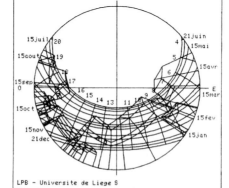

Figure 10   *Comparison of solar masks in the middle of the north-facing garden in front of the project*

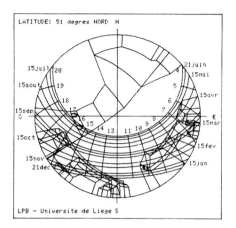

Existing site

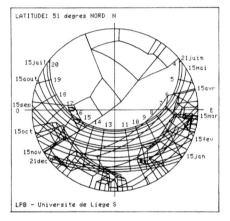

Project 1

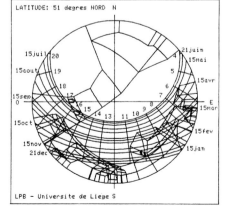

Project 2

Figure 11   *Comparison of solar masks on the living room window of the neighbour to the north-west*

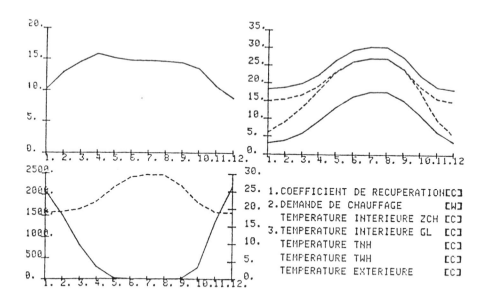

1. COEFFICIENT DE RECUPERATION [C]
2. DEMANDE DE CHAUFFAGE   [W]
   TEMPERATURE INTERIEURE ZCH [C]
3. TEMPERATURE INTERIEURE GL [C]
   TEMPERATURE TNH   [C]
   TEMPERATURE TWH   [C]
   TEMPERATURE EXTERIEURE   [C]

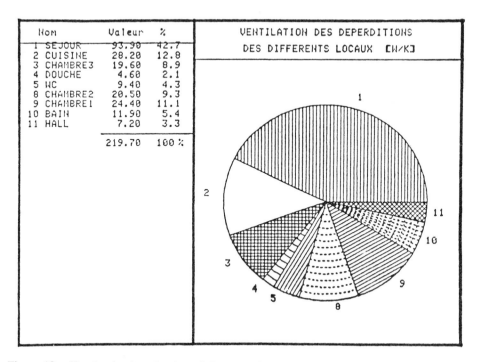

Nom	Valeur	%
1 SEJOUR	93.90	42.7
2 CUISINE	28.20	12.8
3 CHAMBRE3	19.60	8.9
4 DOUCHE	4.60	2.1
5 WC	9.40	4.3
8 CHAMBRE2	20.50	9.3
9 CHAMBRE1	24.40	11.1
10 BAIN	11.90	5.4
11 HALL	7.20	3.3
	219.70	100 %

VENTILATION DES DEPERDITIONS
DES DIFFERENTS LOCAUX [W/K]

Figure 12   *Heating load evaluation of the second project*

PART 3   POLICY AND PLANNING

THE URBAN FUTURE: DOES ENERGY REALLY MATTER?

Susan Owens

Department of Geography and Newnham College
University of Cambridge

Abstract

This paper addresses three basic questions. First, how is spatial structure at the intra-urban scale likely to respond to energy constraints? Second, would it be necessary to intervene to ensure that any response was in the direction of greater 'energy efficiency'? And finally, is it realistic to think that energy considerations could (or should) have more than a marginal impact on urban policy and planning at this scale?

In addressing the first question it is necessary to make predictions about urban evolution and to answer the second we need to identify the characteristics of an energy efficient environment. It is very easy in each case to fall into the trap of 'energy determinism'. Models can help to formalize ideas, but it is essential to employ a variety of approaches and to remember that it is *people* who use energy and who live in 'spatial structures'.

A great deal of uncertainty remains. Nevertheless it has been possible in the past decade to identify certain land use patterns and built forms which apparently have energy advantages. The final part of the paper looks at the constraints involved in translating what is now a large and growing body of theory into policies and achievements in practice.

Introduction

Does energy really matter in urban design? Ten years ago, as the effects of a dramatic increase in energy prices were making themselves felt in many ways, the answer to this question seemed obvious. For many architects and planners, the question was not whether we should improve energy efficiency in the built environment, but how. Since then an enormous amount of work has been done, and very little has been achieved 'on the ground'.

Now in the mid-1980s, the prospects for energy conscious urban development have receded further. Oil prices have fallen almost as dramatically as they rose in 1973/4, removing the incentive (though not the need) to use resources efficiently. Although this 'glut' may advance the onset of the next crisis, and although acid rain and nuclear accidents constantly remind us of the non-monetary costs of energy consumption, complacency has been setting in. At the same time we have experienced, in Britain at least, a reaction against planning, reinforced in rhetoric and legislation during the past seven years of Conservative government. This has implications for all objectives requiring a significant measure of government intervention.

This paper considers the likely significance of energy considerations in urban development, looking first at changes which may be brought about by 'the market' - what might happen anyway - and then at what we would *like* to happen in the built environment from the point of view of energy conservation. The latter involves identifying energy-efficient spatial structures at the intra-urban scale. The most important question, perhaps, is why desirable change does not happen. Why is it that energy seems to be an important consideration for the future, that we can identify a variety of spatial structures in which energy efficiency is compatible with other social objectives, yet we remain a long way from achieving energy-integrated urban design at the intra-urban scale in Britain? The final section of the paper will address these questions.

Energy constraints and urban form

Urban spatial structure became more energy intensive during the period of decreasing real fuel prices which led up to the oil crisis in the early 1970s; the results are obvious for all to see in the urban sprawl which characterizes many Western cities. At the intra-urban scale the absence of energy constraints manifested itself in decreasing densities, concentration of facilities like shops and health care into fewer, larger units and - as a result of these two trends - the increasing physical separation of activities. Heating was provided individually and inefficiently. Energy considerations were ignored in the planning and development process. It is tempting to assume that these trends would be reversed if energy were to become more scarce and expensive in future. Certainly this view appealed intuitively to many observers in the aftermath of the oil crisis, who looked forward with a certain grim enthusiasm to the 'imploding metropolis' (Franklin, 1974).

The metropolis, however, has not imploded; indeed the exodus of people and jobs from major cities in Britain accelerated quite dramatically in the 1970s. It may of course be argued that the 'crisis' was not sustained and that no lasting energy constraints have actually been experienced. But it is increasingly clear that energy constraints could not lead to any simple reversal of urban trends. Energy factors permit or constrain urban change - they do not cause it. To examine their influence on urban form in isolation will almost certainly lead the investigator into the trap of energy determinism.

Exploring the response to constraints

How then might we approach the question of possible changes to spatial structure at the intra-urban scale in response to energy constraints? There are major uncertainties which frustrate attempts to explore this issue and restrict it to the realm of informed speculation. First, we know little about the nature of future 'constraints', though the consensus of opinion is that real oil prices will rise in the medium term, and in transport at least, oil is currently crucial. Secondly, what really matters is how *people* (not urban structures!) respond to energy constraints, but results from work in this area have so far been characterized by a 'frightening lack of uniformity' (Dix and Goodwin, 1982). How elastic is demand for travel and space heating, the two factors which most influence energy demand at the intra-urban scale? And how might individual response, for example to price increases, be related to spatial structure? These are crucial questions, since it is quite possible for energy consumption to be reduced in ways which will have little or no effect on the form of the built environment.

Evidence from a variety of analytical frameworks (reviewed by Dix and Goodwin 1981, 1982) suggests that petrol price increases are unlikely to have a very marked effect on travel behaviour in the short term (Figure 1). Marginal adjustments of trip patterns, especially 'social' trips, are associated with only small changes in petrol consumption. Evidence that people find ways of coping in the short term is provided by 'backtrack' interview surveys of adaptation to cost changes, many of which were conducted in the aftermath of the fuel crises of the 1970s (e.g. Carpenter and Dix, 1980; Corsi and Harvey, 1977), and by the response to an unusual situation in Hobart, Tasmania. Here destruction of a bridge left nearly a third of the urban population effectively stranded from the city centre, and provided researchers with a unique opportunity to study coping strategies in the face of a very sudden 'time-space divergence' (Wood and Lee, 1980).

In the medium term, people try to revert to their former trip patterns, and will resort to other methods to save petrol without loss of mobility (such as changing cars). Thus there is an important distinction between 'traffic' elasticity, which has implications for spatial

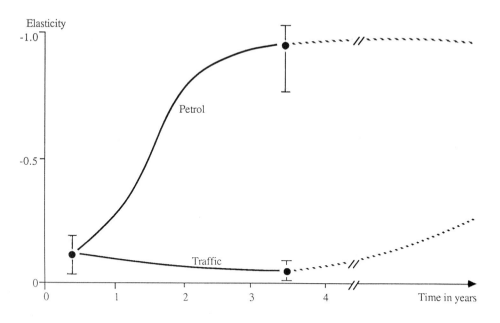

Figure 1   *'Petrol' and 'traffic' elasticities: possible changes over time (source: Dix and Goodwin, 1982)*

readjustment in the longer term, and 'petrol' elasticity which need have no such implications (Figure 1). It is conceivable that people might adjust their travel habits (move closer to work or schools, for example) around the time of 'life shocks' (important transitions between life cycle stages), but there is no really clear empirical evidence to support this hypothesis. However, the possibility of longer term spatial change cannot be discounted, so it is worth exploring further its possible implications at the scale between buildings and cities. It is in this context of exploration that urban models may be useful, as long as their limitations are recognized and the temptation to use them for prediction is resisted.

Travel requirements and urban models

Some of the results of modelling exercises are entirely unsurprising given the input assumptions (especially the implicit assumption that people will respond in certain ways to energy constraints). Increasing the importance of transport costs in the 'trip decision' in a Lowry model, for example, results in closer association between different activities and a reduction in the total amount of travel (Beaumont and Keys, 1982); utility analysis of residential location suggests that higher energy prices are likely to produce residential areas closer to employment centres (Romanos, 1978); and energy constraints in a standard spatial interaction shopping model lead to decentralization of retail facilities in terms of size and location (Beaumont, Clarke and Wilson, 1981). But none of these results can tell us *what might happen* since, as Mogridge (1984) points out, we cannot be confident that response to energy price rises can legitimately be modelled in this way. We should be particularly wary of using a sophisticated form of description to make predictions which may feed into policy.

One or two findings are worth comment, however. It is interesting that utility analysis, superimposed on suburbanization of employment, produces a pattern of 'decentralized concentration' within urban areas, because this pattern emerges fairly consistently from different approaches as an energy efficient way of organizing land uses at the 'intra-urban' scale. Perhaps even more significantly, when gravity type models have been used to compare the transport energy requirements of different land use patterns, the *ordering* of forms in terms of energy efficiency is sensitive to the value assumed for the 'impedence' factor, which itself is logically related in these models to the degree of energy constraint. This implies that we cannot necessarily identify 'intrinsically efficient' patterns, but significantly, some patterns emerge as 'robust' across the range of different assumptions about future energy availability.

Heating and the housing market

In relation to market responses and possible changes in spatial structure, the situation for space heating is more complex than for travel, since fuel substitution is possible to a much greater degree. However, it is interesting to consider how energy constraints in the residential sector might be reflected in the housing market and, ultimately, in spatial structures and the 'fine grain' of urban development. This will depend on the ways in which people adjust to increases in the price of fuel for space heating. They may change fuels, tolerate lower temperatures or eliminate waste, none of which will necessarily have any influence on patterns of urban development. But it is conceivable that the energy advantages of more efficient built forms will be recognized. It is now well known that at the local scale, factors such as siting in relation to micro-climate, the physical arrangement of buildings and built form can make a very significant difference to space heating requirements.

The question is whether recognition of these factors could result in increased demand for energy efficient buildings, induce migration to areas where they already predominate and influence the built form and density of new construction through the housing market. This could in theory encourage a movement towards city centres (where terraces and flats are most likely to be located), or as energy prices rise, people might turn increasingly to semi-autonomous systems, such as solar space and water heating, as these become more economically attractive. This too might encourage relocation, but in a different direction towards lower density areas where such systems may be most viable (Owen Carroll and Udell, 1982). Most significantly, perhaps, for the scale between cities and buildings, there could be demands for new kinds of construction, rehabilitation and redevelopment.

All these are possibilities, but again they are qualified by great uncertainties. Even if energy considerations become much more important in house purchase (and there is little evidence that this is happening in Britain at present), there are so many ways in which residential energy consumption can be reduced that this would not be a sufficient condition to influence spatial structure. We could become much more energy efficient within the same shells.

This is all very unsatisfying. In the short to medium term it seems that energy does not matter very much. People are likely to respond to energy constraints (if indeed there *are* constraints in the short to medium term) in both the transport and domestic sectors in ways which will reduce energy consumption while having little significant effect on spatial structure. The longer term implications are more interesting spatially, but even more uncertain. Given these inevitable problems, the most appropriate way forward must be to abandon attempts to make ever more accurate 'predictions' - we simply do not know enough about the energy future or the way in which people are likely to behave - and concentrate instead on flexible, normative planning based on an intelligent assessment of likely trends. We now turn, therefore, to the more pragmatic question of appropriate urban planning policies for an energy uncertain future.

Energy efficient form at the intra-urban scale

In as far as planners influence transport policy and (together with architects) the density and siting of new development, they have an opportunity to improve the energy efficiency and flexibility of the built environment. What should they aim to achieve? To answer this we need to identify energy efficient spatial structures, focusing here on the scale between buildings and cities. Not only is this scale the subject of discussion at this seminar, but it is a scale at which land use planning, if it is effective at all, may reasonably be expected to have some impact.

Identifying energy efficient forms

These questions can be approached in a variety of ways - through the use of models to explore potential change and to compare hypothetical forms, through empirical measurement of energy use in urban areas with different characteristics, through identification of the spatial requirements of energy technologies and from combination of all these into normative planning and evaluation of specific ideas. All methods have their advantages and problems (for more detail, see Owens, 1986b), but from this diversity of approaches, a degree of consensus about energy efficient forms at the intra-urban scale has emerged.

It is useful to distinguish between energy efficient characteristics of urban form and the forms themselves, since once the desirable characteristics have been identified, they can be found in more than one form.

The characteristics of an environment which is 'inherently' energy efficient, with low useful energy requirements, have much in common with those which allow maximum opportunity for fuel conserving technologies. Compactness and mixing of land use (with clustering of trip ends) facilitate trips by public and non-motorized transport (see, for example, Keyes and Peterson, 1977; Roberts, 1975) and allow the economic introduction of energy efficient CHP/DH systems (Atkins and Partners, 1982; Combined Heat and Power Group, 1979). These characteristics are not incompatible with the small scale exploitation of solar power, even though it introduces constraints on the siting, orientation and spacing of buildings. Passive solar systems can quite readily be incorporated at densities of up to 125 persons per hectare (pph) and could be compatible with higher densities (even up to 200 pph) with design ingenuity (Doggart, 1979; O'Cathain and Jessop 1978; Turrent *et al.*, 1981). To meet a high proportion of a community's energy needs from ambient sources would, however, require much lower overall densities (unless renewable sources were exploited using very centralized high technology), so that some forms of renewable energy future seem at first to be precluded by the kind of compact spatial structures which have many other energy advantages (Owens, 1986b). But even this

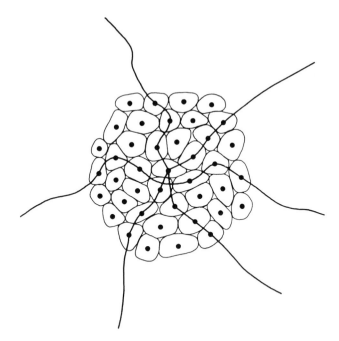

Figure 2   *Compact nucleated urban structure (note: semi-autonomous sub-units need not necessarily be contiguous)*

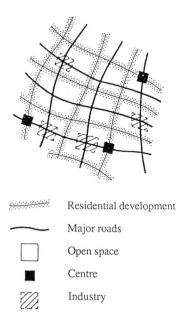

	Residential development
	Major roads
	Open space
	Centre
	Industry

Figure 3   *Linear grid structure (source: Rickaby, 1979)*

potential conflict may be capable of resolution within a 'linear grid' structure at the intra-urban scale.

'Ideal' forms

Two forms seem to be most promising at this scale. One is what Mathieu has called an 'archipelago' pattern, consisting of compact, nucleated urban sub-units of between 10,000 and 30,000 people having 'walking distance' or bicycle scales (Figure 2) (Mathieu, 1978; Thomas and Potter, 1977). Clearly the population of these areas must be large enough to provide the threshold for a range of facilities if they are to be sufficiently 'autonomous' to reduce travel requirements. But it is difficult to define a minimum size since thresholds change over time. In the past they have increased as travel costs have diminished and greater economies of scale have been sought; under energy constraints thresholds may fall again, making smaller units 'viable' and potentially energy efficient, though such predictions are subject to uncertainty. This pattern may not be energy *efficient* if mobility is relatively unconstrained and people choose not to take advantage of their 'local' employment and service opportunities. But it remains a flexible or robust pattern in the sense that facilities would be available if mobility were to *become* restricted in the future.

One problem with the compact nucleated structure is that it does not give the kind of immediate access to green areas which might be desirable for a more 'self-sufficient' community in future (in terms of both energy and food), though this could be achieved at some energy cost by making the urban sub-units non-contiguous. An alternative solution would be a linear grid structure, combining the energy advantages of higher densities and integration of activities with access to open land and the potential for a wider range of life styles and energy systems. This structure, based on the ideas of Lionel March, (March, 1967; Martin and March, 1972), and developed by Rickaby (1979), permits a high linear density of development in which integration of land uses is achieved by concentrating origins and destinations of trips onto a small number of routes (Figure 3). It is an ideal structure in theory for public transport and CHP/DH systems, but because it is 'full of holes' it would be compatible with quite extensive use of renewable energy sources (Rickaby, 1979; Steadman, 1977); it is also compatible with the concept of semi-autonomous units at the intra-urban scale. The band of development in a linear grid would be wide enough to allow dwellings to be located well away from the main route, so that there need be no confusion of this concept with highly undesirable 'ribbon development'.

Discussion of these 'ideal' structures tends implicitly to assume development on a clean slate, but many of the principles could equally well be applied to growth and change. At the intra-urban scale it would be possible in theory to encourage nucleated development around suburban centres and along transport corridors, and to guide growth so that it resulted in greater integration of activities rather than greater separation. Criteria for densities, built form and orientation can normally - again in theory - be applied to both green field and incremental development.

Energy savings

Only rarely will urban designers be working with a clean slate. Nevertheless, it is worth considering the magnitude of the energy saving potential of efficient spatial structures as part of the wider appraisal of the costs and benefits of different ways of improving energy efficiency. The figures in Table 1 are estimates of possible 'savings', comparing an ideal efficient form with a typical inefficient pattern. It must be stressed that some of the figures, especially those relating to transport energy, can only be rough estimates based on numerous assumptions (in models, for example), and Table 1 cannot be read as if savings are simply additive. Furthermore, in practice, change is likely to be incremental, the starting point may not be the 'worst case' and the optimum structure is unlikely ever to be achieved.

But with all these reservations it is clear that some of the savings which might be achieved in a more energy efficient built environment are of a similar order of magnitude to potential savings which are often quoted in other contexts. They compare well, for example, with improvements in vehicle efficiency which might achieve a 20-25% reduction in fuel use by the early 21st century (Banister, 1981; Maltby *et al.*, 1978) and with improved insulation standards which could result in typical space heating requirements being halved (Leach *et al.*, 1979).

The effects of different *kinds* of energy conservation measures will not be cumulative. If fuel consumption in cars is cut by half, potential absolute energy savings from reducing the physical separation of activities will be smaller. If building standards reduce space heating requirements, less in a absolute sense can be gained by promoting energy efficient built forms. This is not an argument to ignore potential savings in any field, but it emphasizes the importance of understanding the costs and benefits of adopting different measures. It has often been assumed that modification to spatial structure would have a

Structural variable	Mechanism	Possible saving
Density/built form	Space heating	200% variation between forms
Density/clustering trip ends	Viability of public transport	Savings up to 20%
Density/land use mix	⌈ Viability of CHP/DH	Energy efficiency improved by up to 100%
	⌊ Travel requirements	Variation of up to 130%
Density/siting/ orientation	Space heating (micro-climate and passive solar)	Savings of at least 20%

Table 1 *Potential energy savings at the intra-urban scale*

relatively high cost-to-benefit ratio, but this has never been demonstrated convincingly. On the contrary, energy efficient environments seem to offer many other social and environmental advantages.

There are obvious uncertainties about the theoretical potential to reduce energy consumption by modification to spatial structure at the intra-urban scale, even before considering the constraints which will prevent the full potential from being realized. While it must be acknowledged that 'ideal' structures are probably unattainable, it has been possible to identify energy efficient development patterns and we should be able to formulate planning and building policies to achieve them. In fact, this has proved very difficult to do in Britain. The following section explores why.

Policies and constraints

Presumably, we would not wish to promote urban forms with social and environmental disadvantages, whatever their energy saving potential. But in fact there are few proposals arising out of energy considerations which are not attractive in other ways. Nucleated or linear grid structures could provide accessibility and amenity as well as flexibility for a range of different energy futures. The implications are that we should be designing urban environments like this anyway, and that their energy advantages are merely a bonus.

Indeed there is evidence that in Britain spatial patterns which are desirable from an energy viewpoint are being advocated in development plans for their social, economic and environmental advantages (Owens, 1986a). But whether energy related policies are explicit or not, they may prove very difficult to implement. In this sense it could be argued that energy 'does not matter', because energy objectives will either be achieved by default, or like many other socially desirable goals they will continue to be defeated by vested interests in the political process. This brings us to the important question of constraints.

Broadly speaking, the policy implications of the energy/spatial structure relationship are that energy should be a legitimate concern for all those involved in shaping the urban environment, including architects, builders and planners, and that energy efficiency, or at least energy flexibility should be a common goal. But this argument, however compelling, makes the major presumption that we work within a framework where intervention and planning themselves are accepted as legitimate. In reality we have recently seen rejection rather than reinforcement of these values: 'deregulation' is in vogue. Any proposals implying greater planning or regulatory powers in the built environment may, at least for the time being, be virtually impossible to implement. This is a major constraint on immediate action which cannot be overlooked, though it need not be permanent.

Secondly, it is essential that improving the energy efficiency of the built environment should be part of a wider shift in philosophy towards the use of energy and other resources in society as a whole. The movement towards energy conscious urban design will be doomed to failure unless it can be set within this broader framework. Such a framework is noticeably lacking in Britain, where government energy policy is still very much supply orientated and conservation is seen largely as something to be brought about in the market place, rather than through intervention (in line with the broader 'deregulation' philosophy). The government has noticeably failed to give any encouragement to planning authorities to take energy considerations into account and the Department of the Environment has actually deleted energy related policies from several structure plans (see Owens, 1986a and b for more detail). Since structure plans set the framework for local plans and development control, which are the important planning tools at the intra-urban scale, this attitude is another major constraint on energy conscious urban development.

Similar arguments apply with local authorities, where a 'corporate' approach to energy conservation has much to recommend it. In those cities in the United States where energy conscious urban design has been most actively pursued, it has normally been an integral part of a comprehensive energy conservation programme. Many local authorities in Britain have appointed 'energy managers', but the concept of the role is narrow, usually restricted to energy efficiency within local authority buildings such as offices and schools. Control over energy supply and over the various fields of local authority administration is more centralized than in the United States, where energy is supplied by private utilities and there is greater local autonomy in relation to such functions as, for example, building regulations. In Britain there is less scope for integration of relevant policies at local level to form an effective 'energy management programme'. This adds a significant institutional constraint to the ideological ones already mentioned (see also Sheldrick and Cooper, 1987).

If these ideological and organizational problems could be overcome, it should in theory be quite straightforward to integrate energy considerations into the planning and development process. In planning, energy efficiency should be one of many goals, energy related policies should be included when alternatives are considered and energy flexibility should be among the criteria for evaluation. Development control at the intra-urban scale would then, in theory, become more energy sensitive. Building regulations should be progressively adjusted so that the fabric becomes more energy efficient. Any measures in danger of slipping between the planning and building regulations (for example, control on orientation or block design) should be explicitly included - probably in the former, which would allow more flexibility of interpretation.

In practice none of this has been achieved. Changes to the building regulations have been relatively timid, and there has been very little explicit recognition of energy in the planning process - which is itself much more 'messy' than any simplistic model of it might suggest. Constraints, in addition to those already mentioned are many, and the will to overcome them is likely to be inversely proportional to the perceived seriousness of the energy supply situation. Both memories and the ability to look beyond the immediate future tend to be rather restricted when it comes to the need to use energy efficiently.

Constraints may be illustrated by examples of policies at the intra-urban scale which have been strongly advocated in the interests of energy conservation. One is the encouragement of facilities within walking and cycling distance of homes or readily accessible by public transport. This a central tenet of most 'energy efficient' patterns, including nucleated and linear grid structures. It is clear, however, that the social advantages of easily accessible facilities have long been recognized and voiced but if those who benefit from centralization and economies of scale are politically more powerful than those who lose, planners with mainly negative powers can exercise little effective control over relevant location decisions. Similar points could be made about public transport. Energy considerations may make very little difference to the outcome.

A second example is the need to site and orientate groups of buildings so as to take maximum advantage of micro-climate and especially to make use of passive solar energy (an issue discussed in much more detail in other papers presented at this seminar). Generally this is viewed as a measure which would deliver significant benefits at very little cost. But there are no regulations to ensure energy efficient siting and orientation. Interestingly, the Greater London Council (GLC) included policies in its draft alterations to the Greater London Development Plan (GLC, 1983) which would provide a suitable framework for energy considerations in development control. As well as containing broader energy related objectives, there are specific policies, including explicit support for the development of renewable energy resources and conservation, and a recognition of the spatial implications at the 'micro' level. One policy, for example, states that:

> "In considering the design and layout of new developments, attention will be given to the potential contribution of renewable energy". (GLC, 1983, p.121),

and another proposes that:

> "Due consideration should be given in the detailed design and layout of all residential, commercial and industrial developments to the desirability of using energy efficiently. In particular, attention should be given to built form, building design, materials, orientation, overshadowing, topography, vegetation, microclimate and other considerations insofar as these affect the consumption of energy" (GLC, 1983, p.122).

The GLC, however, no longer exists; abolition is an effective constraint on an authority's ability to carry out its good intentions! Transfer of planning powers to the boroughs does not bode well for this kind of innovative thinking; several of the boroughs considered the energy related policies to be 'inappropriate' when they commented on the draft plan (Gibbs, 1984). The GLC case throws up one further interesting example of institutional rigidity as a constraint. The GLC wanted to make provision for CHP/DH; the Central Electricity Generating Board complained in their comments on the draft alterations that such matters were not the responsibility of the GLC (Gibbs, 1984).

Another kind of institutional inertia frustrates attempts at energy conscious 'micro-level' planning. There can only be a significant effect on spatial structure if major developers take the relevant ideas on board and are prepared to innovate. So far they have shown themselves to be deeply conservative with respect to design and layout of development, unwilling to risk anything that may be seen as unorthodox. While it is encouraging if smaller developers are prepared to experiment, this is not going to have any marked overall effect. It is interesting in this context to consider what happened when the Davis (California) Energy Plan was adopted. The stringent new building code was initially opposed strongly by developers who were convinced that it would lead to expensive, aesthetically unpleasing housing, and that orientation requirements would mean lower densities and reduced profits. Their fears proved unfounded, since housing costs increased by only one or two per cent and there was no change in appearance. Now the builders are among the foremost advocates of the new energy conscious approach! (Craig, 1982; Lee, 1980; Owens, 1986b).

This problem of conservatism relates back to the question of the demand for energy saving features in the housing market. Almost certainly other factors matter much more when buying a house, so there is no 'consumer pressure' on developers to take energy into account. The situation will be exacerbated by the fall in oil prices. The 'market', therefore, will not ensure longer term energy efficiency in the building stock, but further intervention, though highly desirable in this situation, is unlikely for the reasons already outlined. However sophisticated we make our models and designs, we will continue to be faced with these fundamental constraints on action.

There are genuine physical constraints too. How can we achieve decentralization in linear grids or nucleated structures when what we have is suburban sprawl and inner city decay? If the answer is through incremental change, then we must remember that the building stock turns over at a rate of 1% per annum. The rate of change is faster in some areas, but even then much development takes place on relatively small sites, where siting and orientation are likely to be determined by non-energy considerations, and many planning authorities have a large bank of inherited commitments which permit little flexibility in forward planning and development control.

Concluding comments

Much of what is written about energy and urban form makes only passing reference to these constraints in an almost 'statutory' paragraph. But it is unlikely that any progress will be made unless constraints are considered in an integrated way, rather than as an appendage to more theoretical work. We need to continue with fundamental research, and to show what might be achieved in an ideal world, but to press on regardless in the hope of a more sympathetic climate is not enough. We need simultaneously to be aware of political and other constraints, to incorporate them where they cannot be overcome and to be prepared to challenge them when they can.

References

Atkins, W.S. & Partners (1982). *CHP/DH Feasibility Programme: Stage 1, Summary Report and Recommendations for the Department of Energy.* Epsom, Surrey: W.S. Atkins & Partners.

Banister, D. (1981). *Transport Policy and Energy: Perspectives, Options and Scope for Conservation in the Passenger Transport Sector.* Town Planning Discussion Paper No. 36, University College London.

Beaumont, J.R., Clarke, M. and Wilson, A.G. (1981). Changing energy parameters and the evolution of urban spatial structure. *Regional Science and Urban Economics*, Vol. 11, pp. 287-315.

Beaumont, J.R. & Keys, P. (1982). *Future Cities: Spatial Analysis of Energy Issues.* Chichester: Wiley.

Carpenter, S.M. and Dix, M.C. (1980). *Perceptions of Motoring Costs and Responses to Cost Changes*, 123/WP. Oxford University Transport Studies Unit.

Combined Heat and Power Group (1979). *Combined Heat and Electrical Power Generation in the United Kingdom.* Report to the Secretary of State for Energy. Energy Paper No. 35. London: HMSO.

Corsi, T.M. and Harvey, M.E. (1977). Energy crisis travel behaviour and the transportation planning process. *Transportation Research Record 648*, pp. 30-36.

Craig, P.P. (1982). Energy, land use and values; the Davis experience. In R.W. Burchell and D. Listokin (eds.) *Energy and Land Use.* Centre for Urban Policy Research, Rutgers University, pp. 510-525.

Dix, M.C. and Goodwin, P.B. (1981). Understanding the effects of changing petrol prices: a synthesis of conflicting econometric and psychometric evidence. *Proceedings of the PTRC Annual Meeting*, Warwick, July.

Dix, M.C. and Goodwin, P.B. (1982). Petrol prices and car use: a synthesis of conflicting evidence. *Transport Policy Decision Making*, Vol. 2, pp. 179-195.

Doggart, J.V. (1979). *Eastern Flank - Energy Issues*. Unpublished discussion paper, Milton Keynes Development Corporation.

Franklin, H.M. (1974). Will the new consciousness of energy and environment create an imploding metropolis? *American Institute of Architects (AIA) Journal*, August, pp. 28-36.

Gibbs, S., Greater London Council (1984). Personal communication, 30th July.

Greater London Council (GLC) (1983). *Draft Alterations to the Greater London Development Plan*. London: GLC.

Keyes, D.L. and Peterson, G. (1977). *Urban Development and Energy Consumption*. Working Paper No. 5049-1.5. Washington D.C.: The Urban Land Institute.

Leach, G., Lewis, C., Romig, F., Buren, A. van, Foley, G. (1979). *A Low Energy Strategy for the United Kingdom*. London: Science Reviews Ltd.

Lee, H. (1980). *The Role of Local Governments in Promoting Energy Efficiency*. Discussion Paper E-80-12. Cambridge, Massachusetts: Energy and Environmental Policy Center, John F. Kennedy School of Government.

Maltby, D., Monteath, I.G., and Lawler, K.A. (1978). The UK surface passenger transport sector: energy consumption and policy options for conservation. *Energy Policy*, Vol. 6, pp. 294-313.

March, L. (1967). Homes beyond the fringe. *Royal Institute of British Architects Journal*, August, pp. 334-7.

Martin, L. and March, L. (1972). *Urban Space and Structures*. Cambridge University Press.

Mathieu, H. (1978). The role of urban planning in relation to overall adaptation to the new energy context: some broad lines of a possible strategic orientation. Paris: Centre du Recherche d'Urbanisme. (Presented at *First International Conference on Energy and Community Development*, Athens, Greece, July).

Mogridge, M.J.H. (1984). Review of *Future Cities: Spatial Analysis of Energy Issues* by J.R. Beaumont and P. Keys, *Progress in Human Geography*, Vol. 8.

O'Cathain, C. and Jessop, M. (1978). Density and block spacing for passive solar housing. *Transactions of the Martin Centre for Architectural and Urban Studies*, Vol. 3, pp. 137-163.

Owen Carroll, T. and Udell, E.B. (1982). Solar energy, land use and urban form. In R.W. Burchell and D. Listokin (eds.) *Energy and Land Use.* Centre for Urban Policy Research, Rutgers University, pp. 156-177.

Owens, S.E. (1986a). Strategic planning and energy conservation. *Town Planning Review,* Vol. 57, No. 1, pp. 69-86.

Owens, S.E. (1986b). *Energy, Planning and Urban Form.* London: Pion.

Rickaby, P. (1979). *An Energy Efficient Strategy for the Completion of Milton Keynes.* Centre for Configurational Studies, Open University, Milton Keynes.

Roberts, J.S. (1975). Energy and land use: analysis of alternative development patterns. *Environmental Comment,* September, pp. 2-11.

Romanos, M.C. (1978). Energy price effects on metropolitan spatial structure and form. *Environment and Planning A,* Vol. 10, pp. 93-104.

Sheldrick, B. and Cooper, I. (1987). Intermediate scale energy initiatives in Britain: exemplary projects, not strategic planning. In this volume.

Steadman, P. (1977). Energy and patterns of land use. *Journal of Architectural Education,* Vol. 30, No. 3, pp. 1-7.

Thomas, R. and Potter, S. (1977). Landscape with pedestrian figures. *Built Environment Quarterly,* Vol. 3, No. 4, pp. 286-290.

Turrent, D., Doggart, J. and Ferraro, R. (1981). *Passive Solar Housing in the UK.* A Report to the Energy Technology Support Unit, Harwell. London: Energy Conscious Design.

Wood, L.J. and Lee, T.R. (1980). Time-space convergence: reappraisal for an oil short future. *Area,* Vol. 12, No. 3, pp. 217-222.

INTERMEDIATE SCALE ENERGY INITIATIVES IN BRITAIN: EXEMPLARY PROJECTS, NOT STRATEGIC PLANNING

Bill Sheldrick

School of Geography, University of Leeds

Ian Cooper

Eclipse Research Consultants, Cambridge

Abstract

This paper presents an overview of some energy-related initiatives currently being taken at the level between individual buildings and cities in Britain. The range of possible activities on this front along with obstacles to international comparisons of activity at this level are explored. It is suggested that opportunities for and constraints on such initiatives are more productively viewed against the specific national and local circumstances in which they arise. Examples of activity at the intermediate level in Britain are offered. These appear to be driven more by social welfare considerations, by wishes for economic regeneration and for community development than by ambitions to reduce the absolute consumption of finite fossil fuels or even to promote a relatively more efficient consumption of energy. Against this background, the likelihood of comprehensive, locally-based, energy efficiency programmes evolving in the near future is examined. It is concluded that, as long as a centrally defined energy policy prevails whose rhetoric deems market forces to be the final arbiters of energy-related activity, attempts at comprehensive energy planning at the level of the local built environment will remain marginalized.

Introduction

Although the subject area addressed at this seminar is very broad - energy use in the built environment at a scale intermediate between buildings and cities - the chosen focus of attention is much narrower and more specific: the simulation, analysis and prediction of the performance of buildings. One recurrent concern centres around the technical means most appropriate for achieving a desired end: urban developments and configurations which are energy efficient. Such discussion revolves around the physical form of buildings, their spatial locations, the inter-play between these factors, their effects on energy use patterns and on resultant disaggregated and aggregated fuel consumptions.

187

However, this focus runs the danger of ignoring other important factors. Energy analysis of built forms, both as academic and theoretical concerns, is not a new phenomenon. Does its comparative lack of acceptance in Britain reflect a fundamental flaw within existing applications? Or is it that such exercises are weakened by being divorced from the political, social and financial realities in which they would need to operate?

In response to these questions, for most of this paper we draw back from debate about physical and technical factors which surround energy modelling. We stand back in order to consider those other factors which will be crucial to achievement of energy efficiency on this front - the socio-economic and political contexts in which energy planning at the intermediate level has to occur in Britain. Progress on this front will be difficult to establish and maintain, no matter how robust or sophisticated the technical means and physical models available, unless the socio-economic circumstances and the political structures in which they have to be applied are understood and taken into account.

Our aim is to present examples of some of the energy-related initiatives which are currently occurring in Britain. We examine the forms in which these initiatives are emerging and the settings in which they are taking place. We identify the agencies involved in them and the clientele which they are trying to serve. We discuss their objectives, their *modus operandi*, the motives which underpin them, and their strengths and weaknesses. We also describe the political climate and legal planning framework within which these British initiatives are having to operate. Our intention in assembling this set of case studies of current activity is not simply to catalogue or dissect what is already happening. Instead, our interest lies in looking beyond design and planning possibilities in order to begin to map out the social, economic and political terrains into which locally based, energy-related initiatives directed at the built environment are born and in which they will have to survive or perish. Our purpose in doing this is to indicate some of the pressing non-technical issues we believe need to be confronted if energy planning at this scale is to thrive in Britain.

Range of possible activities

Before reviewing present British practice, it is useful to identify:

i)   the levels at which energy-related initiatives directed at the built environment at the intermediate scale can occur;

ii)   the measures which it is possible to take at these different levels.

These levels and measures can then be used to construct a backcloth against which to gauge the initiatives which are currently being pursued both here in Britain and abroad. The outline of a matrix illustrating the variables which influence the energy requirements of spatial structures at different scales has been offered by Owens (1985), see Figure 1.

STRUCTURAL VARIABLE	SCALE	LEVEL OF ACTIVITY
Settlement pattern (e.g. rank-size, geometrical arrangement etc.)	REGIONAL	
Communication network between settlements	SUB REGIONAL	
Size of settlements (area)		
Shape of settlement (circular, linear etc.)		LAND USE
	INDIVIDUAL	
Communication network within settlement (radial, grid etc.)	SETTLEMENT	PLANNING
Interspersion of land uses	NEIGHBOURHOOD	
Degree of centralization of facilities		
Density	BUILDING	
Layout (estates etc.)		
Orientation (of buildings or groups of buildings)		BUILDING
Siting (in relation to microclimate)		DESIGN
Design		

Figure 1   *Variables influencing the energy requirements of spatial structures at different scales (adapted from Owens, 1985)*

Our interest here is focused on those which occur at the level of groups of buildings and neighbourhoods. Owens represented these variables, from 'design' thorough to 'interspersion of land uses', as points lying along a single continuum of increasing scale. But it is important to discriminate between the nature of the variables depicted here: this affects where, when and by whom, decisions about their implementation are made during the process of designing a new, or altering an existing, built environment. From this perspective, it is evident that measures taken to make individual or aggregations of individual premises energy efficient by means of 'design', through 'siting' and 'orientation', to 'layout' and 'density', can all result from decisions taken by those responsible for building design or management. Conversely, measures taken to make settlements or regions energy efficient by means of the 'degree of centralization of facilities' or the 'interspersion of land uses' lie beyond the control of building designers and managers in the field of land use planning. Thus, in looking at initiatives undertaken in this country and elsewhere, it will be necessary to keep a clear distinction between *conservation* measures implemented (through design or retrofitting) of individual or groups of buildings and *land use* measures applied at a higher scale through planning mechanisms.

The range of conservation measures which can be taken when designing or retrofitting individual or groups of buildings is now well documented. Orthodox statements on those that are regarded as cost-effective in Britain can be found, for example, for new housing in the Construction Industry Research and Information Association's Report 105 (1984), see Figure 2, and, with direct government backing, for new and existing domestic premises in an Energy Efficiency Demonstration Report from the Energy Efficiency Office (1985), see Figure 3. As these publications reveal, consensus opinion in Britain suggests that worthwhile measures for housing include:

-    improved insulation (if possible applied evenly to all appropriate building elements);

-    draught-proofing and weather stripping;

-    control, and possibly use, of solar gain;

-    consideration of thermal mass and surface temperatures to achieve comfort conditions;

-    ventilation and condensation control;

-    improved design of, and controls for, space and water heating systems.

Despite this level of agreement amongst those offering guidance, as Olivier (1986) chronicles, British building standards and practice continue to lag behind those of the United States and Canada.

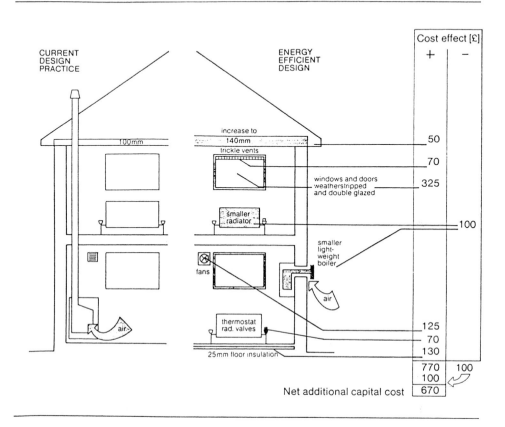

Figure 2 *Capital cost implications of energy efficiency measures for housing (source: CIRIA, 1984)*

Practical advice on the influence of siting, layout, density and landscaping on energy efficiency is much harder to come by in the UK. The Building Research Establishment is aware of this deficiency and has two Digests on 'Local climate and site development' in preparation (Keeble, 1985). The Energy Technology Support Unit has commissioned work on site layout for the Department of Energy to support its Passive Solar R & D Programme (NBA Tectonics, 1986). Nevertheless, the most detailed guidance on energy efficient microclimate design and estate or neighbourhood layout that is publicly available comes from North America, e.g., American Institute of Architects (1978); Brown *et al.* (1982); McPherson (1984), see Figure 4; and Tabb (1984), see Figure 5.

Features of the Energy Saving Design which can be identified within the Demonstration House – 6 Colvin Close, 68-72 Lawrie Park Road, London SE26.

1. Draught-stripped front door.

2. Draught lobby.

3. Draught-stripped kitchen door to reduce water vapour entering rest of the house.

4. Three taps on sink – tap with yellow top supplies solar heated water.

5. Warm air outlet.

6. External wall-cavity insulation plus Thermalboard dry-lining.

7. Passive solar gain here. Some heat stored in floor and wall and released later. This area could be turned into Conservatory by addition of internal wall.

8. Draught-stripped windows. Double glazing.

9. Rear draught lobby.

10. Draught-stripped back door.

11. (View from outside or above.) Solar panels for water heating. Solar heated water stored in cylinder in roof space.

12. Warm Air Heating/Ventilation unit. Takes in fresh air, mixes with recirculated air, heats and distributes through ducts.

13. Draught-stripped bathroom door to reduce water vapour entering rest of the house.

14. Gas water heater. Fed from Solar cylinder so as to reduce amount of gas required to achieve required temperature.

15. Three taps on bath and washbasin. Taps with yellow tops provide solar-heated water.

16. External wall-insulating blockwork with Thermalboard inside and cladding externally.

17. External wall-insulated timber frame, cladding externally.

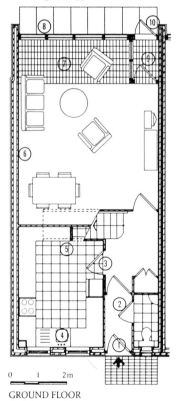

GROUND FLOOR

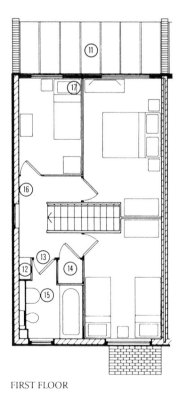

FIRST FLOOR

Figure 3   *Energy efficient design features for housing (source: SLC Energy Group, 1985)*

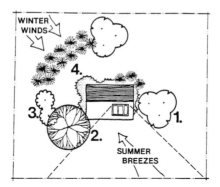

Planting design - Minneapolis, Minnesota

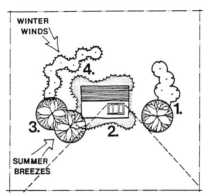

Planting design - Atlanta, Georgia

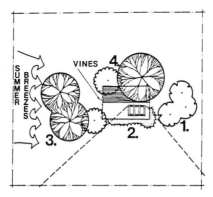

Planting design - Phoenix, Arizona

Figure 4   *Examples of advice on planting for solar control* (source: McPherson, (1984), copyright 1984, American Society of Landscape Architects, Washington D.C., all rights reserved, used with permission)

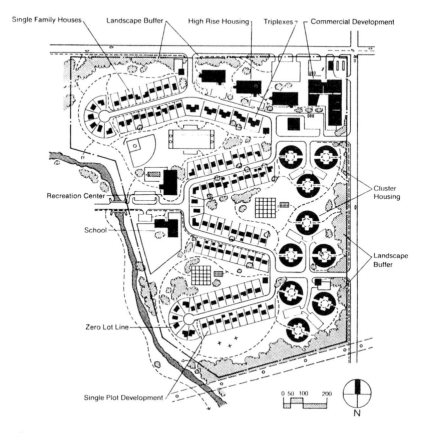

Figure 5   *A composite solar energy-based neighbourhood plan* (source: P. Tabb, *Solar Energy Planning*, copyright 1984, reproduced with permission of McGraw-Hill)

This discrepancy in the availability of these different types of design guidance on either side of the Atlantic is also apparant in the energy initiatives being implemented in the respective countries. Six years ago, Green (1980) argued in his *Programme for the Inner City* that US federal initiatives at the level of conservation measures - particularly those aimed at low income groups in response to pioneering projects by local community activists - were a relevant guide to the approaches, techniques and opportunities that could be employed in Britain. Such initiatives, he recorded, had begun to show a clear link between the achievement of energy efficient buildings and the creation of jobs - a theme subsequently proselytized with great enthusiasm in Britain by the Association for the Conservation of Energy (1983). But, as Sheldrick (1985b) noted, signal differences prevent direct comparisons between the UK and USA in terms of their respective approaches to

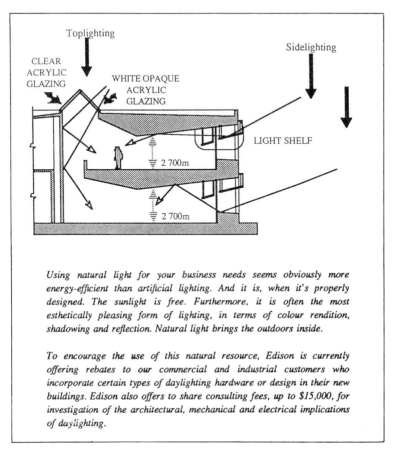

Toplighting

Sidelighting

CLEAR
ACRYLIC
GLAZING

WHITE OPAQUE
ACRYLIC
GLAZING

LIGHT SHELF

2 700m

2 700m

*Using natural light for your business needs seems obviously more
energy-efficient than artificial lighting. And it is, when it's properly
designed. The sunlight is free. Furthermore, it is often the most
esthetically pleasing form of lighting, in terms of colour rendition,
shadowing and reflection. Natural light brings the outdoors inside.*

*To encourage the use of this natural resource, Edison is currently
offering rebates to our commercial and industrial customers who
incorporate certain types of daylighting hardware or design in their new
buildings. Edison also offers to share consulting fees, up to $15,000, for
investigation of the architectural, mechanical and electrical implications
of daylighting.*

Figure 6 *Guidelines and incentives for daylighting new buildings in North America
(source: Southern California Edison, 1985)*

energy conservation at the central and local government levels. Amongst these are:

- constitutional differences (such as the separately defined existence of state
  governments and their independent powers to raise finance);

- contrasting relationships between local authorities and the energy supply industries;

- and differences in the resources options and energy generation capacities open to the
  two countries.

In the United States, the latter issue alone can make conservation measures more attractive
to public utilities, not just in terms of reducing demand from the existing building stock
but through climate-sensitive design of new buildings as well, see Figure 6.

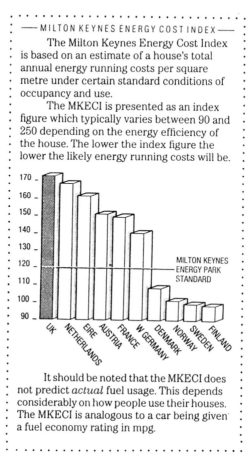

Figure 7   *Milton Keynes Energy Cost Index (source: MKDC, 1986a)*

Similar differences can exist at the scale of land use measures too. Foreign initiatives at this level have been discussed by Owens (1985), especially in relation to controls over the location of facilities and growth points at the city/regional scale in US cities and in terms of regionalized energy supply via district heating and combined heat and power in Scandinavia. But she too warned against direct comparisons because of differential perceptions, opportunities, and constraints. In Britain, it is difficult to identify concrete examples of initiatives at the level of land use planning. In Milton Keynes, the Energy Park is being heralded as an area of the city that will set new (British) standards in energy efficiency both through individual building design via its Energy Cost Index (MKDC, 1986a), see Figure 7, and through "landscaping to save energy" (MKDC, 1986b). Similar

	Additions	Losses	Total stock at year end	Net gain
1973	306.3	103.7	19,415	202.6
1974	281.3	69.1	19,627	212.2
1975	323.2	79.8	19,870	243.4
1976	324.6	70.8	20,124	253.8
1977	312.1	61.4	20,374	250.7
1978	291.5	50.1	20,615	241.4
1979	234.5	47.3	20,822	207.2
1980	244.5	40.6	21,025	203.9
1981	206.1	48.8	21,178	157.3
1982	180.3	41.7	21,317	138.6
1983	204.6	29.3	21,494	175.3

Table 1   *UK dwelling stock, 1973-83 (000's of dwellings) (adapted from Central Statistical Office, 1985)*

concerns can be seen at work in Bourneville Solar Village (Franklin Company Consultants, 1985). But, in the British context, at least, these two schemes have to be recognized as exceptions.

Among the judgements which can be made on the basis of the case studies that follow is some indication of which of Owens' variables for making spatial structures more energy efficient at the intermediate scale are actually being operated upon in this country at present. Those at the scale of land use planning are, almost without exception, not being broached. Even at the level of conservation measures, only those relating to the fabric of individual units of accommodation are really receiving attention. Siting (particularly in relation to microclimate), orientation, density and layout, all these opportunities for energy efficiency are, with few exceptions, being ignored or dismissed. In part, this state of affairs is simply a reflection that the emphasis found in each of the case studies we reported is on rehabilitation rather than new-build. And this, in turn, arises from the low absolute rates of replacement of the existing building stock in Britain which, as Table 1 illustrates, was running as low as 175,000 units a year in the domestic sector by 1983. But such figures only offer a partial explanation. Just as importantly, the emphasis on conservation measures detected in the initiatives also accurately reflects both the harsh social, economic and political realities in which they are operating and the constraining effect which these have on their underlying objectives and motives.

Case studies

Introduction

Four examples of initiatives targeted at the intermediate level are now briefly examined with regard to their objectives, scale of operation, financing, participants, and their achievements and weaknesses. Marked variations are discernible in these initiatives which reflect differing responses to local circumstances. Despite this variance, they also display common features. All are concerned primarily with domestic consumers. Each operates in areas deemed to fall outside the workings of the market mechanism. All are focused on retroactive measures as opposed to green field developments. In each case, reactive attempts are being made to ameliorate existing situations. Significantly, in none of the initiatives described here is energy conservation, energy efficiency, or reduced energy consumption explicitly identified as part of the underlying rationale.

The order in which the case studies are presented reflects their varying degrees of involvement, both in terms of scale of operation and in the range of measures attempted. The first two cases represent initiatives targeted on estates within their respective cities, though differing in the comprehensiveness of their insulation and heating packages. The latter two are concerned with larger scale, borough-wide (but still intermediate) developments. But, once again, these too can be differentiated according to the array of measures being applied and in terms of the contrasting ability of their proponents to implement them. The initiatives presented here are not the only ones currently being pursued in Britain. For example, we could have included discussion of Cardiff Energy Action, the priority estate programme promoted by the Department of the Environment, or the Dudley Energy Conservation Area. But the case studies reported here do offer a clear indication, both of the kinds of initiatives being conducted in the UK at present, and of their defining characteristics.

1) Heatwise Glasgow

Heatwise Glasgow was established in 1983 through the joint efforts of Scottish Neighbourhood Energy Action and Glasgow District Council (Nec, 1985). It functions as a local energy project, by providing loft insulation and draught-proofing to low income households using the resources of the Manpower Service Commission's Community Programme to pay for labour. The scale of its operations and its financial backing set Heatwise apart from most other energy projects. This enables it to offer a completely free, door-to-door service for all council tenants, regardless of their income, in those areas identified from the 1981 census data as suffering from multiple deprivation.

Heatwise operates with three explicit objectives:

1) to tackle fuel poverty by undertaking insulation and draught-proofing work, providing information and advice on heating and welfare benefit entitlements;

2) to create employment, both through providing immediate job prospects, and improving long term opportunities through training and skills courses;

3) to involve the local community in these issues and activities.

All three objectives are considered to have equal weight within the organization. Accordingly, a project will not be established in an area, regardless of deprivation or need, if local participation is not forthcoming. Within the organization, the aim is to establish a project a month, each with a life span of approximately one year. To date fifteen projects have been initiated, although three have reached the end of their life span, see Figure 8. The percentage of the dwelling stock represented by council dwellings (as of 1984) is indicated in Figure 8, for each city district in which a Heatwise project has been operating.

Heatwise does not have to sell its services to its clients. Instead, it has been brought into existence by various funding sources, the two most essential of which are the MSC and GDC. The former pays for labour and the latter covers the salaries of core personnel and the bulk of the cost of materials. Money is also forthcoming from the Department of Energy in the form of seedcorn and project start-up grants, from the Department of the Environment via insulation grants, and from the Department of Health and Social Security as single payments for draught-proofing materials. The financial support of GDC entitles the project to various grants made available from the European Economic Community. Heatwise's structure and operations are designed to maximize the available grants which, because of regulations, would otherwise be denied or inaccessible to Glasgow District Council.

During its first year and a half, Heatwise has been responsible for draught-proofing over 10,000 dwellings and insulating over 1,000 lofts out of a potential 63,000 dwellings in the

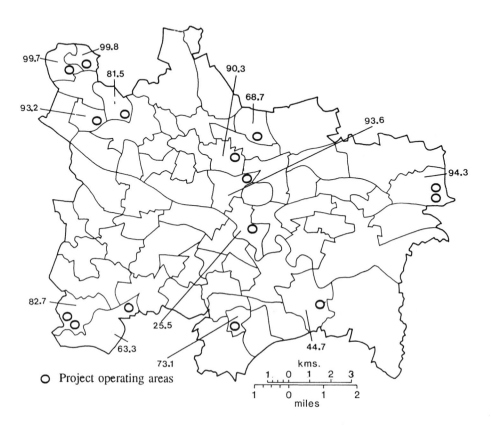

Figure 8 *The city of Glasgow and the operating areas of Heatwise Glasgow*

areas in which they have been operating. Approximately 350 people are employed, the majority of whom are in the age range of 18 to 22. At present, because of success in mobilizing both political and local support for their operation, the budget for Heatwise is doubling annually. Likewise, there is a waiting list of tenants' associations wanting projects to be established. Despite these successes, Heatwise is not in a position to tackle one of the underlying causes of fuel poverty: tenants still have to rely on expensive-to-operate heating systems despite other ameliorative measures taken on their behalf.

2) Westgate Hill, Newcastle

Newcastle City Council has been at the forefront of local authorities involved with energy initiatives, particularly those demonstrating a community orientation. Its Energy Advice Unit was the first of its kind in the UK and was a precursor to the establishment of Neighbourhood Energy Action (NEA, 1985). 'Keeping Newcastle Warm' was one of the first local energy projects. Underlying this involvement has been a variety of concerns - improving the local economy, job creation, protecting the local authority's investment in its dwelling stock, tackling condensation problems, and the affordability of heating systems. Beyond this has been a political reality: the necessity for the council to be seen to be doing something positive.

Since 1979, the council has been systematically upgrading its own dwelling stock under a Priority Ranked Assessment (PRA) programme. This has involved the use of a quasi-technical, subjective aggregation of three factors: condensation and mould growth, heating system adequacy, and running costs. The PRA programme stemmed from an internal report indicating that 20,000 dwellings (approximately 40%) were suffering from condensation and mould growth to varying degrees. In principle, those estates scoring highest on the rank ordering were to receive top priority in any particular year's investment programme.

Regardless of ranking, however, no tower block was included within the PRA programme until 1982. Westgate Hill Estate, comprising 360 flats in three 20-storey tower blocks located within the inner city of Newcastle, was the first high rise development included within the tower block improvement programme, see Figure 9. This estate had been constructed in 1962-3, with electric underfloor heating to the living room, hall and part of the kitchen in each flat. The flats suffered from severe condensation and mould growth in bedrooms, bathrooms (rooms with no heating) and kitchens. A submission by the Local Authority's Energy Advice Unit to the Department of Health and Social Security resulted in the estate being designated in 1983 as 'hard-to-heat' for the purposes of social security, on the basis that its heating system was disproportionately expensive to run.

The Council's internal departments collaborated to devise a comprehensive heating and insulation improvements package, encompassing technical, consultative, and monitoring measures. At Westgate Hill, the electric underfloor heating system was disconnected and replaced with electric storage radiators operating on the cheap night-time tariff. The new

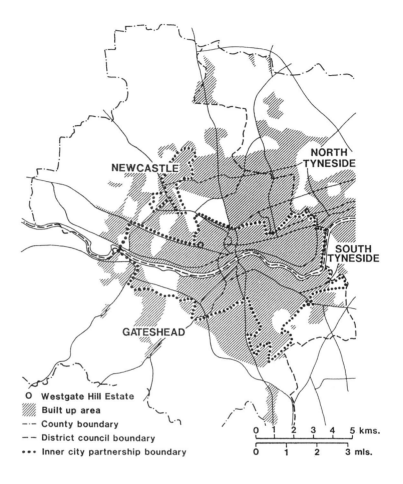

Figure 9　*City of Newcastle upon Tyne and the Westgate Hill Estate*

heating system was extended throughout the flat. The water heating was converted to the night-time rate and the hot water cylinder was given extra lagging. The external walls were internally dry lined, reducing their U-value from 1.2 to 0.35 W/m²°C. The glazed area in the living room was reduced from 80 to 40% of the external wall area, with secondary glazing installed. Window fittings were serviced and doors and windows draught-proofed. The tower block roof was insulated. Follow-up exercises included leaflets designed by the council explaining how the new controls and heating system operated, individual visits by both the Energy Advice Unit and the local Electricity Board, and monitoring of consumption and a consumer survey. The package was neither revolutionary, nor innovative, in terms of the measures installed, but it was exceptional in the comprehensive manner in which problems were tackled.

In Figures 10a and 10b, the distribution of expenditure on electricity (at March 1984 prices) for a full year, both before and after the improvement works were undertaken at Westgate Hill, are illustrated. An increased frequency amongst the lower expenditure brackets, with a larger concentration of all consumers in the middle brackets, is evident after the improvements. Mean expenditure declined from £333 p.a. in 1980/1 to £253 p.a. in 1983/4.

Another significant development was the increase in consumers using the installed heating system. In 1980/1, approximately 46% of tenants were consuming less than 250 units of electricity through the underfloor system, including one of the three consumers in the highest expenditure bracket (the underfloor system was metered separately). After the heating and insulation improvements, less than 8% of tenants were consuming less than 750 units (the increased figure was to account for the conversion of the water heating system to the night-rate tariff). This change is indicated by the shaded areas in Figures 10a and 10b. As well as benefitting (on average) from improved thermal comfort and reduced fuel bills, the likelihood of resorting to inappropriate heating appliances (e.g. paraffin and LPG), with their attendant problems of condensation and explosion, is reduced.

Finance has been a central feature in shaping the PRA programme. Its continuation during a period of fiscal stringency and reduced capital expenditure allocations reflects the Local Authority's political commitment to pursuing comprehensive solutions to energy problems. A policy decision to allocate 20% of its annual capital housing budget for this purpose measures the size of this commitment.

During the consultation exercises conducted prior to the Local Authority embarking on the heating and insulation improvements, the tenants were adamant that they did not want another electric heating system installed. Instead they wanted a district heating scheme. Despite a commitment within the PRA programme to tenant consultation, the tenants' wishes were overruled, eventually on the grounds of capital cost (a district heating system was approximately three times more expensive). The programme has resulted in the thermal fabric and performance of the building being improved and an apparent general satisfaction on the part of tenants with both the running costs and the comfort levels achieved (Sheldrick, 1985a). Although electricity consumption has actually increased,

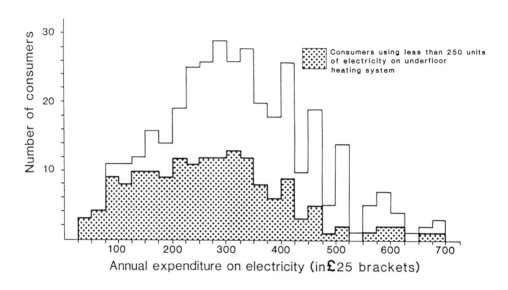

Figure 10a *Distribution of 1980/1 expenditure on electricity (at March 1984 prices)*

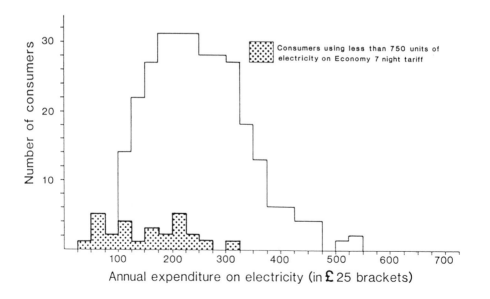

Figure 10b *Distribution of 1983/4 expenditure on electricity (at March 1984 prices)*

electricity bills have fallen. The success of the package of measures undertaken at Westgate Hill has been used both by the Council to sell it to reluctant tenants on other estates, and by the Electricity Board to other local authorities.

3) Lewisham Energy Plan

The Greater London Council's Popular Planning Unit provided finance in 1983, initially over one year, for two workers who were to prepare a Community Energy Plan for the London Borough of Lewisham, see Figure 11. Underlying the Popular Planning Unit's concern was an intention to enable tenants to participate more fully in decisions affecting their lives by providing them with an access channel (GLC, 1984). Funding was subsequently renewed up to April 1986 when the GLC was itself abolished. Whatever the possibilities and potential identified by formulating this Energy Plan, the role of the

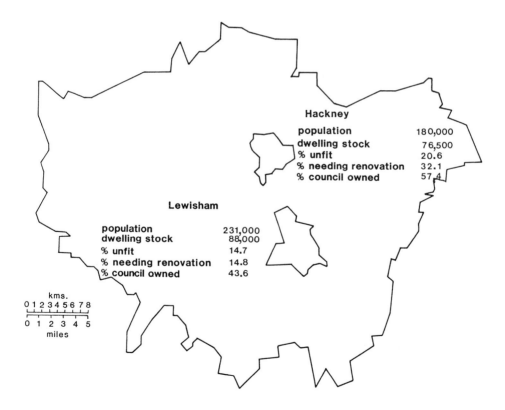

Hackney	
population	180,000
dwelling stock	76,500
% unfit	20.6
% needing renovation	32.1
% council owned	57.4

Lewisham	
population	231,000
dwelling stock	88,000
% unfit	14.7
% needing renovation	14.8
% council owned	43.6

kms.
0 1 2 3 4 5 6 7 8
0 1 2 3 4 5
miles

Figure 11 *The London boroughs of Lewisham and Hackney*

workers involved was to be that of outsiders, bringing external influence to bear, since the Borough Council of Lewisham was not originally involved in either the funding or direction of the Energy Plan.

The focus throughout the existence of the Energy Plan was on the Council's housing stock which makes up approximately 60% of all dwellings in Lewisham. Work undertaken included classification and modelling exercises in order to identify the distribution and frequency of house types within the Borough, surveys of the range of problems and hardships faced by tenants, estimates of the potential for improvements and their costs. The scope of activity was not restricted solely to investigating such demand characteristics, it also focused on the implications of alternative methods of meeting local demand, particularly by means of CHP.

Progress with implementing the Energy Plan has always been dependent on the Council adopting the outsiders' proposals. The workers were not in a position legally, politically or financially to intervene directly in order to implement their plans. Consequently, their efforts were targeted on establishing their credibility within the Borough Council. Regular contact occurred with various departments - Housing, Social Services, Planning and Architects, the Chief Executive's Office, and with elected members. Briefing documents were prepared, meetings held, and training programmes for housing managers initiated. While the Energy Plan workers considered these exercises to have been successful after their first year of operation, actual achievements on the ground were not evident. Sympathy and platitudes were forthcoming but these were not necessarily accompanied by any practical action.

Between November 1984 and April 1986, the workers shifted their approach. The emphasis was switched from focusing on the local authority, towards encouraging tenants to take up the issues themselves. To this end, special courses and training sessions were held, with the workers providing advice, technical support, and other back-up as necessary. Energy audits and reports were prepared to enable tenants and tenants' associations to present their cases to the DHSS and to the Borough Council for increased welfare benefit entitlements, and for heating and insulation improvement packages. The scale of focus was thus shifted from the Borough as a whole to individual estates within Lewisham.

During the two and a half years of the project's existence the actions taken by the Energy Plan's workers have resulted in additional heating-related welfare benefits for tenants throughout the Borough, including the designation of a number of estates as 'hard-to-heat', the quantification of heating related problems, the proposal of various remedies that would bring heating costs in dwellings in line with tenants' available incomes, the production of a 'Tenants' Charter for Warmth' which has been adopted by the local federation of tenants' groups and which is being considered for acceptance by the Borough Council. Accordingly, tenants, council officers, and elected members have been mobilized and their awareness of energy related issues increased. A proposal for an Energy Advice Unit is presently being considered by the Borough Council as a means of continuing the type of work initiated by those responsible for the Energy Plan.

However, it has to be acknowledged that the switch in focus from the Borough to individual estates and the preoccupation with their problems represents a reduction in the original conception of the Energy Plan. It also accurately reflects the reality of its funding and existence. Without the political ability to force the Council to act upon their proposals, and denied financial resources to undertake the improvements themselves, the workers' initiatives are dependent on the acceptance and actions of others.

4) London Energy and Employment Network

The London Energy and Employment Network (LEEN) was established in 1983 under the Greater London Enterprise Board (GLEB) - originally the job-creating arm of the GLC - to operate throughout the Greater London area. It has pursued two related objectives: to promote a rational energy policy for London and to stimulate resultant employment opportunities. LEEN has identified six specific areas of work. Of particular interest here are the establishment of community-based energy projects and the development of energy conservation areas. In pursuit of its objectives, the emphasis within LEEN has been on initiating a range of practically orientated projects that would illustrate the constituent parts of a rational energy strategy.

In July 1984, LEEN concentrated its efforts on the London Borough of Hackney (see Figure 11) - statistically one of London's most deprived with a population of approximately 180,000 and a catalogue of social, economic, and employment hardships typical of those confronting inner city areas. Of Hackney's total stock of 76,500 dwellings, 21% were considered unfit for human habitation, while a further 32% were in need of renovation. On a percentage basis, Hackney figured worst in England (see House of Commons, 1985).

A conference, chaired by the Deputy Leader of the Council, was organized and attended by local politicians, council officers, representatives of tenants' groups, local organizations, law centres, fuel boards and advice agencies, and other interested parties. Workshops generated a list of suggestions for action and a steering committee was convened to implement them and measure progress. The steering committee identified various short and longer term measures that Hackney Council could undertake. Success was considered by the steering committee to be dependent upon the implementation of effective practical projects, the provision of advice and information, and the arrangement of financing packages. An early achievement was the publication of a Right to Warmth Charter and its subsequent adoption as Hackney Council policy. The Charter became the focus of the steering group's activities. The committee has since given way to a full time co-ordinator within the Borough whose remit is to develop further energy initiatives and liaise with external organizations.

LEEN's role within this project was neither to do the actual work itself nor to impose itself on the area of Hackney. Rather it was to facilitate the initiative, to inject enthusiasm, provide back-up, co-ordination, liaison and advice. Among the outcomes of the Hackney project have been the development of funding packages for heating and insulation programmes, the mobilization of local political support for energy issues, the establishment of a local database and models of energy use in dwellings that allow priorities for measures and particular sections of the housing stock to be drawn up, and the Right to Warmth Charter. LEEN has begun to replicate the approach adopted in Hackney in other London Boroughs, although future success will be dependent both on the degree of political support that can be engendered and on the continued existence of LEEN. The London Energy and Employment Network has survived the abolition of the GLC although its funding has been reduced.

Commentary on the case studies

The four case studies reported above demonstrate both variations and common characteristics in terms of their scale, the degree of intervention practised, the nature of involvement of the local authority with the initiatives, and the extent of their financial support. Similarities and differences can also be discerned in their objectives and the approaches adopted.

The scale of involvement described illustrates initiatives targeted both at the level of individual estates and borough-wide. The focus remains fixed, however, at a scale less than the city, but greater than the individual building. Further, the initiatives are not being used to realize national objectives but quite specifically local ones. Improved heating, thermal comfort, building fabric, employment prospects, and welfare benefit entitlements are all tackled in order to benefit the local community. The measures undertaken vary from draught-proofing and loft insulation to comprehensive heating and insulation packages, even, on occasion, to identifying alternative methods of meeting energy demand. Where the problem of 'expensive-to-operate' heating systems cannot be addressed directly through replacement, then a strong emphasis is placed on securing additional welfare benefit entitlements in order to help households to pay for expensive fuels. All the initiatives express an explicit commitment to collective or corporate intervention rather than to relying on individual responses to perceived pricing signals and to the operation of the market mechanisms.

The degree of participation by local authorities in the initiatives ranges between direct involvement, through working in conjunction with external organizations, to providing financial support for work to be undertaken outside the authority. Despite their involvement, none of local authorities are attempting to impose solutions, however energy efficient, on reluctant occupants. Local tenants' groups and associations, community organizations, and other interested parties are being consulted and retain the right to refuse proposed thermal improvements.

Differences in underlying objectives are shown in the contrasting approaches adopted in each of the initiatives - employment, improved housing infrastructure, and local involvement. All of them embody concern for social equity both within their approaches and for targeted clientele. Low income consumers, particularly those receiving welfare benefits or living on fixed pensions, are common targets. Priority is being given to what are seen as the worst areas in each case, by Priority Ranked Assessment as in Newcastle, or by concentrating on inner city areas, on hard-to-heat estates, or areas otherwise designated as being in special need. The funding of individual initiatives displays a diverse array of sources, arrangements, and budget levels. But they all include some contribution from the host local authority despite the financial stringencies currently facing local government. Rather than financial climate being cited as an excuse for not embarking on such initiatives, a more pro-active stance is being adopted. Funds that are available are being utilized while other sources and packages are continually being explored.

It needs to be stressed, however, that none of the initiatives reported here are concerned solely - or even primarily - with energy conservation, energy efficiency, or reducing fuel consumption. In each case, the concern with energy issues overlaps other objectives. Sometimes it acts as a catalyst, enabling other issues to be pursued simultaneously which might otherwise not be being tackled. Regardless of the particular approach adopted in each of the initiatives, only one attempt to use theoretical energy analysis for calculations was discovered. This was being used in the Lewisham Energy Plan, that is, by the very group least able to implement its recommendations.

Newcastle's PRA was a subjective ranking derived from factors that posed the greatest hardships for the tenants. The proposed solutions did not stem from theoretical calculations, or from trying to model heat loss or the energy efficiency of retrofitting measures. Instead it was based on more poignant realities. First, did the proposed solutions reduce the incidence of condensation? Testing the package under what the council described as 'worst conditions' indicated that it did. Secondly, were the two political realities that have influenced much of Newcastle's heating and insulation improvements - affordability and visibility - sufficiently addressed and apparent? A heating system may perform efficiently and insulation standards may be efficacious but a tenant is still unlikely to use the system if the cost of doing so is seen as being too high: heating has to be affordable. Moreover, because the local ruling party has already lost one by-election to an independent candidate standing on an 'anti-dampness' platform, the council is now concerned to be seen to be taking effective action on heating related problems.

Neither LEEN's initiatives in conjunction with Hackney, nor Heatwise in Glasgow, have involved use of energy analysis or modelling, although there are plans being developed for a model to identify priorities for work in Hackney in the future. This particular initiative was instigated in the first instance as a high profile, crisis intervention measure: longer term measures were then seen as arising out of this. In Glasgow, the prime concerns were different: Heatwise is an attempt to maximize impact and available funding for the least possible cost to the city council.

Each of the case studies has been described as exhibiting weaknesses in the way individual initiatives are operating. Nevertheless, it has to be remembered that they are at the forefront of what is currently being put into practice in Britain. For this reason, they represent realized exemplary projects and practices. As such, they should be compared with the energy chapter included in the revised Greater London Development Plan, submitted by the Greater London Council to the Department of the Environment in 1984. This chapter embodied the Council's attempt to be pro-active in the field of local energy policy. It identified policy presumptions in favour of renewable energy developments, rejection of the siting of nuclear power stations in London, ear-marking of a specific area for a CHP/DH scheme based on the old Barking Power Station, and retention of Thames bankside power stations for future extensions of the CHP network.

This attempt by a strategic planning authority to quantify both its energy demand and methods of supply generated antagonism and dissent at both central and local government levels. Individual London boroughs saw the old power stations along the Thames as potentially valuable riverside development sites. The Electricity Council informed the GLC that matters relating to generation were for the Central Electricity Generating Board and the appropriate Government minister to decide, not the GLC.

The Secretary of State did not rule on the revisions to the structure plan. This was overtaken by the abolition of the GLC. However, compared with the *conservation* measures implemented in individual case studies reported here, the GLC's energy chapter represented strategic planning by defining the implications for land use of London's future energy requirements. And, if it had been approved, the chapter would have acquired a formal legal significance within Britain's development control process.

Underlying this energy chapter was the perception that the GLC did have a strategic energy role. Attempts to incorporate such considerations within structure plans elsewhere have not been particularly successful. Essentially, they represent a challenge to the hegemony of the fuel industries and central government in determining national energy policy. This challenge, however implicitly, attempts to reverse the trend of centralization of energy supply that has existed since 1947.

In this context, the initiatives of LEEN, Lewisham, Newcastle, and Heatwise are no challenge. Instead they illustrate incremental measures that can be bolted on to the existing system without calling it into question. Indeed they can be seen as supportive because they allow the worst failings of central government's reliance on market mechanisms and pricing policy to be mitigated. By intervening to offer support to those most disadvantaged, they allow the fuel industries to continue without having to alter either their presumptions or practices. Adoption of an approach similar to that of the GLC would be tantamount to endorsing an energy policy formulated from the bottom up. Such a development would provide local authorities with a strategic role in energy issues - a role that is not presently available to them nor currently encouraged by central government.

Conclusions

As our review of energy-related initiatives is meant to make clear, only a small subset of the variables which Owens has identified as influencing the energy requirements of spatial structures are currently being manipulated in British 'energy efficiency' practices. Typically, low level measures concerned with the conservation characteristics of aggregations of individual buildings are receiving attention: higher level design factors involving site layout and land use planning considerations are not.

In part, this situation stems from the present emphasis on rehabilitation, both because of the deteriorating state of Britain's stock of domestic and non-domestic premises and the low rate of replacement of its infrastructure. But it also derives from the lack of government-endorsed, concrete advice on what Britain designers and planners should be trying to achieve on these fronts. In this vacuum, even Milton Keynes' Energy Cost Index for housing, let alone the GLC's energy chapter, looks radical and takes on the significance of pro-active, 'bottom up' formulation and implementation of energy policy.

Too often, within the practice of modelling and identifying energy efficient design, built form and land use patterns, there is an unquestioned assumption that increased thermal efficiency is a 'good thing'. And, again too often, the focus adopted becomes transfixed on the physical form of individual buildings or aggregations of them. Wherever the focus espoused is primarily on 'energy', then out in the political arena modelling and design will remain marginal concerns and deservedly so. For energy is not to be valued for its own sake, but for the services that it facilitates - warmth, leisure, mobility, production. Within this context, the issues which need to be addressed are not thermal efficiency, energy consumption, or even reduction in fuel consumption per se. As the evidence of Westgate Hill reveals (*increased* fuel consumption after the installation of a comprehensive heating and insulation package), we should be wary, in a society where many have limited access to resources, of focusing too fixedly on the notion of trying to reduce absolute consumption levels.

Building design and layout do have significant economic, political, social and environmental ramifications. Recognizing the conjunction between energy and services, social welfare, and infrastructure concerns, highlights its salience in issues such as alleviating fuel poverty and hardship, improving employment prospects, regenerating the local economy, protecting investment in the building stock, and increasing local accountability and social equity. These are not marginal concerns. Nor does pursuing them exclude modelling input. But it may require a shift in emphasis within the exercises in which they are used and in the perspectives of those who operate them.

Connections between energy and societal objectives are increasingly being made at the local level. The energy chapter within the GLC's revised development plan was an attempt to examine issues of the kind listed here within the context of strategic land use planning. Current political circumstances have determined that, for the time being at least, this foray will not be continued. But, as the recent *Charter for Energy Efficiency* (1986) - published by a consortium of local authorities, trade unions, voluntary sector organizations, and community associations - and as the *London Energy Action Plan* published by LEEN (1986), show, this debate has not disappeared. Instead, continued attempts are being made to focus the energy debate on these wider concerns and to get energy issues onto the political agenda.

At the local level, Neighbourhood Energy Action has been campaigning for local energy plans. If introduced across the country, such a strategy would require a change in policy both towards energy and local government. The existing formal definition of central-local relations is not itself a stumbling block to such developments. However, trends with both energy and local government policy since 1947 have been towards increasing centralization of decision-making. Local strategic planning in most spheres has been eroded in the 'national interest' and by the increasingly onerous financial climate within which local government operates. Legal impediments to the emergence of a local strategic energy role in the U.K. are actually few. Instead, what is required is a shift in political will in order to engender both commitment and direction to locally-based participation. Local authority involvement with in-house activities could be a prelude to a wider, more strategic role. Some evidence of this potential already exists (Sheldrick, 1984). But the local authorities involved in this way represent, at present, only a very small minority. The increased commitment and visibility of central government with energy efficiency since the advent of the Energy Efficiency Office does not particularly address the needs of local authorities or the domestic sector. Instead the EEO's emphasis has been on high profile public relations and promotion, particularly in relation to the industrial sector. This has effectively excluded local authority participation. By concentrating on the establishment of local projects and, in practice, by-passing the potential contribution of local authorities, central government is offering a particular and limited definition of the nature and potential of locally-based, energy-related initiatives. It is stressing their exemplary nature, rather than using them as a means of generating a pro-active and strategic *local role* in the energy debate.

References

American Institute of Architects (1978). *Regional Guidelines for Building Passive Energy Conserving Homes.* US Department of Housing and Urban Development.

Association for the Conservation of Energy (1983). *The Employment Generation Potential of a Major Conservation Programme.* London: ACE.

Brown, G. *et al.* (1982). *Inside Out: Design Procedures for Passive Environmental Technologies.* New York: John Wiley.

Central Statistical Office (1985). *Annual Abstract of Statistics.* London: HMSO.

Charter for Energy Efficiency Group (1986). *The Charter for Energy Efficiency.* London: CEE.

Construction Industry Research and Information Association (1984). *Energy Efficient New Housing.* London: CIRIA.

Franklin Company Consultants (1985). *The Making of a Solar Village and a Demonstration House in Bourneville.* Birmingham: Franklin Company Consultants Ltd.

Greater London Council (1984). *Planning for the Future of London.* London: Department of Transportation & Development, GLC.

Green, D. (1980). *A Programme for the Inner City.* London: National Council for Voluntary Organizations.

House of Commons (1985). *Debates 20/11/85*, Vol. 87, c232w. London: HMSO.

Keeble, E. (1985). *Local Climate and Site Development: Parts 1 and 2*, Draft Digests. Garston: Building Research Establishment.

London Energy and Employment Network (1986). *London Energy Action Plan.* London: LEEN.

McPherson, E. (ed.) (1984). *Energy-conserving Site Design.* Washington D.C.: American Society of Landscape Architects.

Milton Keynes Development Corporation (1986a). *Energy World: an International Exhibition of 50 Energy Efficient Houses.* Milton Keynes: MKDC.

Milton Keynes Development Corporation (1986b). *Energy Park News*, Issue No. 2, p. 1. Milton Keynes: MKDC.

NBA Tectonics (1986). *A Study of Passive Solar Housing Estate Layout.* Energy Technology Support Unit Contract No. S-1126. London: NBA.

Nec, T. (1985). The amazing multi-funded show. *Third Sector*, April, pp. 6-7.

Neighbourhood Energy Action (1985). *Coming in from the Cold.* Newcastle: NEA.

Olivier, D. (1986). *Energy Efficiency and Renewables: Recent North American Experience.* Milton Keynes: Energy Advisory Associates.

Owens, S. (1985). Energy demand: links to land-use and forward planning. *Built Environment*, Vol. 11, No. 1, pp. 33-44.

Sheldrick, B. (1984). Local authorities and energy conservation: the structure of their involvement. *Environment and Planning B*, Vol. 11, No. 1, pp. 42-67.

Sheldrick, B. (1985a) *Hard to Heat Estates: a Review of Policy and Practice.* Working Paper: DHSS 267 BS.10/85, Social Policy Research Unit, Department of Social Administration and Social Work, University of York.

Sheldrick, B. (1985b). An energy efficiency programme for UK local authorities. *Energy Policy*, Vol. 13, No. 5, pp. 485-488.

SLC Energy Group (1985). *Energy Efficient Housing.* Energy Efficiency Demonstration Scheme Report. London: Energy Efficiency Office.

Southern Californial Edison (1985). *Daylighting for New Construction.* California: SCE.

Tabb, P. (1984). *Solar Energy Planning.* New York: McGraw-Hill.

PART 4   CASE STUDIES

GLAZED COURTYARDS: AN ELEMENT OF THE LOW-ENERGY CITY

Dean Hawkes and Nick Baker

The Martin Centre for Architectural and Urban Studies
University of Cambridge

Abstract

For a number of years research at the Martin Centre has explored the environmental and energy-saving potential of glazed internal courtyards in buildings in the British climate. As a result, the technical implications of such structures are now well understood. This paper describes the application of this technical knowledge to a specific design problem. In 1985 the Scottish Heritable Trust, in association with The Architects' Journal, sponsored a competition for the design of an office building close to the centre of York. Competitors were also invited to make proposals for the improvement of an adjacent block of existing nineteenth century buildings. The commended design submitted by Stephen Greenberg and Dean Hawkes was centred upon the exploitation of glazed public spaces as a fundamental element of the technical design of both the new building and the improvement of the existing buildings. This paper describes the design and presents the results of computer simulations of its environmental and energy performance. In addition to the technical discussion, the paper argues that the approach allows an appropriate response to the economic and architectural issues which arise in the renewal of cities.

Introduction

Twenty years ago Leslie Martin and Lionel March published their seminal paper, *Land Use and Built Forms*, in which they first made a comparison between the land use properties of alternative court and pavilion forms of development (Figure 1). This demonstrated that the court form would always achieve a required density of development in fewer storeys than the pavilion when subjected to identical daylighting constraints. From this study there developed a whole series of investigations into aspects of urban planning and building design (Martin, 1972; Martin *et al.*, 1972), (Figure 2).

Dean Hawkes and Richard MacCormac (1978) extended this theme in the research of the Cambridge school by demonstrating the energy saving potential of glazed courtyards. In that study it was shown that designs for office buildings based upon central glazed courts -

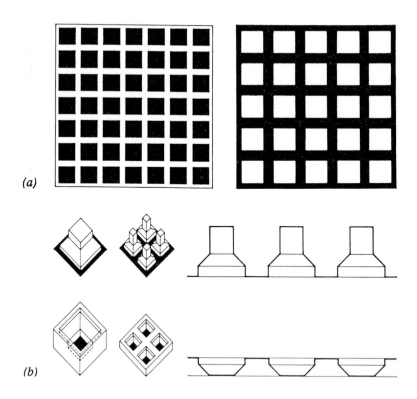

Figure 1   *Comparison of land use potential of pavilion and court forms*

> *(a) A development covering 50% of the site plotted as pavilions and in court form. The contrast in the ground space available and use that can be made of it is immediately apparent.*

> *(b) The generalized pavilion form and the modified antiform at the same scale containing the same amount of built volume and on the same site. The heights are approximately in the ratio of 3:1 (source: Martin and March, 1966)*

or *atria* as they have since become popularly named - can provide a high quality working environment in the British climate at considerable energy savings when compared with air-conditioned designs. By making maximum use of daylight and natural ventilation in summer, temperatures in such a building can be maintained within acceptable comfort standards, without recourse to air-conditioning. Its compact form, with the added benefit of passive solar gains into the court, or atrium, means that winter heating requirements are low.

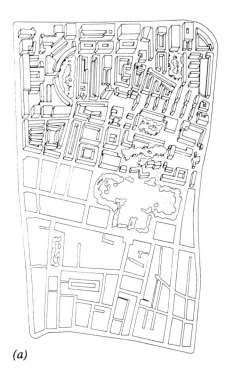 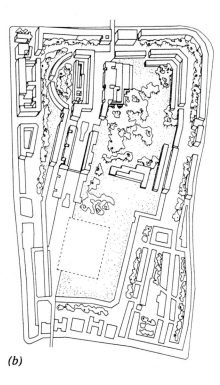

(a)   *(b)*

Figure 2   *(a) The existing plot layout and building development in an area of London that might be regarded as an environment room, but it is sub-divided by roads and the limited size of the building plot increasingly forces development upward.*

           (b) The same area as that in (a). The road network is now enlarged and runs around the boundary of the area. Theoretically an entirely new disposition of buildings is possible and the illustration shows exactly the same amount of floor space in a new form. Tall buildings are no longer necessary: the buildings themselves have a new freedom for development and a considerable area of open space is discovered (source: Martin, 1972).

Baker and Hawkes used dynamic thermal modelling techniques to confirm the predictions made by simpler methods in the earlier work (Baker 1983a & b; Hawkes, 1983). These studies investigated in some detail the environmental conditions in the courtyard itself (Figure 3) and the energy implications of alternative modes of natural ventilation (Figure 4). Matthews (1984, 1985) further extended the work by proposing that glazed roof structures may be used with considerable environmental, energy and commercial benefits, in the rehabilitation of blocks of existing buildings which are found in great numbers in the centres of British towns.

The aim of this paper is to show how this line of research was applied in the production of a commended design submitted in a national architectural competition, held in 1985, for the design of an office building in the City of York (Greenberg and Hawkes, 1986).

Arcades and the morphology of the city

In his monumental study of the urban arcade as a building type, Johann Freidrich Geist has linked its modern origins to the political upheaval of the French Revolution, but, of greater relevance to the modern situation, also shows that it was the product of commercial and climatological considerations:

> "The need for public, undisturbed space was recognized by speculators and exploited by industry ... The amount of traffic on the narrow Parisian streets took on dangerous and threatening proportions at this time. Carriages and carts battled pedestrians. This unequal conflict was fought on poorly paved streets without drainage which were transformed by rain into a sea of mud."
> Geist (1983).

The commercial arcade rapidly became one of the most important elements of the nineteenth century city. Geist in his catalogue lists no fewer than 303 examples constructed between 1786 and 1920. The attractions of a sheltered, traffic-free environment for commercial uses were clearly fully appreciated both socially and financially and many cities developed extensive networks of arcades, often extending over a number of blocks (Figure 5). In the twentieth century the construction of new arcades declined, but those which have survived are now enjoying new prosperity and can be clearly seen as the respectable ancestors of the modern shopping centres which are springing up in many cities.

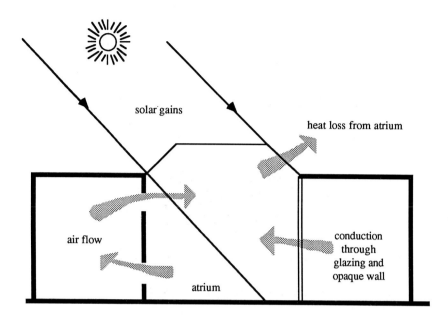

Figure 3   *Environmental conditions in an atrium*

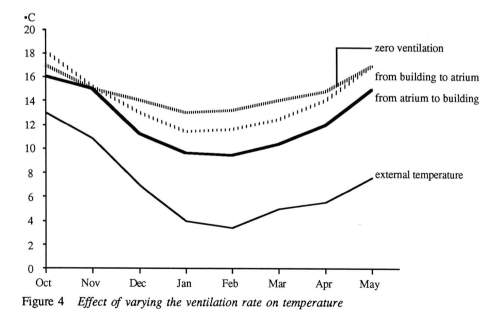

Figure 4   *Effect of varying the ventilation rate on temperature*

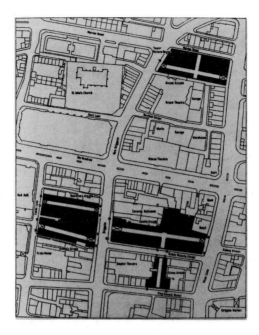

Figure 5   *Leeds, sites of Thornton's Arcade, Queen's Arcade, County Arcade and Cross Arcade*

York Riverside

The competition for the development of a site between the River Ouse and Skeldergate at York (Figure 6) was promoted jointly by The Scottish Heritable Trust and The Architects' Journal. The major part of the brief was for an office building on a vacant site, to contain at least 2500m^2 of net usable office space, *plus* proposals for other uses, such as bars, restaurants, sports facilities and boat or river-related facilities. In addition, competitors were invited to make proposals for the development of an adjoining site to the north. This contains a number of existing buildings around its perimeter, mainly from the nineteenth century, with a series of yards at the centre. The key statement in the brief was that

> "The promoter believes that a site of this significance should have on it a building which will stand alongside the many fine buildings of all centuries in the city. He believes the new project should be a striking example of architectural excellence of this age and that the materials used for the building should reflect the very latest advances in the art and technology of building." (*The Architects' Journal*, 1985)

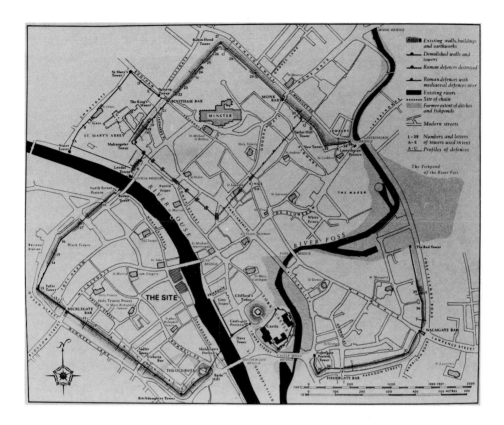

Figure 6   *York Riverside Competition: site location plan*

A number of issues were identified as the basis for the development of this design. First was the nature of the response to the promoter's requirement quoted above. Second, and related to this, was the belief that the building should not be seen as an isolated architectural statement, but should be integrated into the fabric of the existing city. Finally was a concern that the design should both address the specific requirements of the site and brief, and demonstrate a set of generic propositions which could be applied to other sites and briefs.

The question of the role of technology in determining the nature of architecture has been the focus of debate throughout history. In the nineteenth century the nub of the issue was succinctly put by Pugin in his aphorism:

"Ornament construction, do not construct ornament."

This view, which was shared by many theorists and practitioners in the nineteenth century (see Macleod, 1971), was attacked early in the present century by Geoffrey Scott (1914), in his rejection of the 'Mechanical Fallacy' and the debate has assumed new significance in recent years as an element of the widespread re-evaluation of the tenets of the Modern Movement.

The most obvious manifestation of the Puginian viewpoint in present day practice is the 'Hi-Tech' school, with its conspicuous display of structure and services. But the role of building technology, and particularly of a scientifically-based understanding of technical performance, can be more than skin-deep. In approaching this design the aim was to apply this understanding to the production of a building which offered advanced technical performance, particularly with respect to environment control, within a built form and use of material which reflected the immediate context and the deeper architectural themes of York in particular and the English tradition in general.

At the centre of the design for both the new building, and the rehabilitation of the adjacent block of existing buildings, is the idea of the glazed courtyard (Figure 7). This performs a number of functions within the design. First it operates as the principal element of the environmental system of the building. Through it natural light is brought into the centre of the block, both new and existing. In the summer months the courtyard, or more accurately *arcade* in this instance, serves to induce natural ventilation through the 'stack-effect' and in winter it becomes a source of 'free' pre-heating for the incoming air for the mechanical ventilation system by exploiting passive solar gains through the south-facing glazed wall above the roof of the Skeldergate block. Summer-time overheating is avoiding by automatically operated external louvres on the southern faces of the structure (Figure 8).

The arcades of the two blocks provide an extended covered public space leading south from Bridge Street parallel to the river. This opens up additional frontage for shops, restaurants and other commercial uses and could possibly be extended further to the south as far as Skeldergate Bridge, linking the newly developing uses on this bank of the river, and becoming a protected promenade comparable with those provided by the great nineteenth century arcades.

In detail the design for the new building consists of two concrete framed blocks, one, facing Skeldergate, of three storeys, and the other, looking over the river, of four storeys plus a basement at the level of Queen's Staithe. These are surmounted by a steel framed

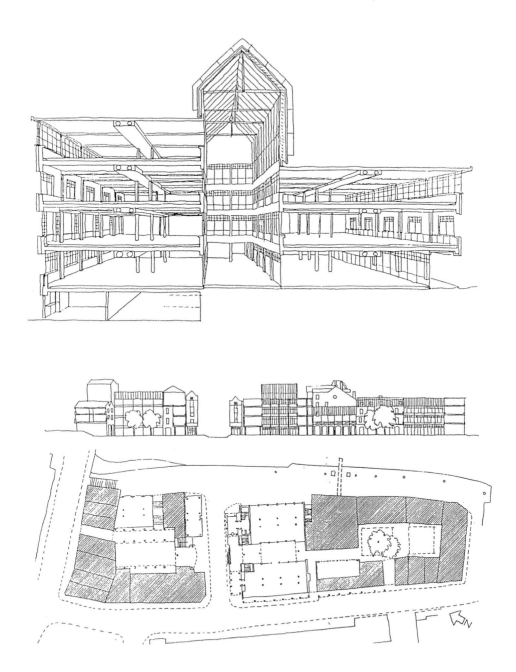

Figure 7   *York Riverside Competition: site plan and section*

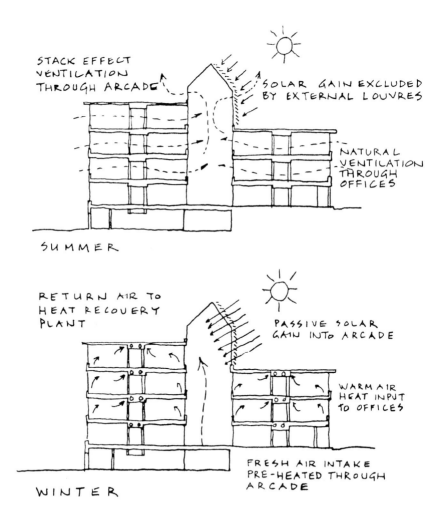

Figure 8   *York Riverside Competition: winter and summer modes of environmental control*

roof structure which supports a flat roof over each block and develops in section to form the pitched roof over the arcade. The facades consist of a self-supporting brick skin which is tied back to the frame through a layer of thermal insulation. All of the window frames are fixed to the masonry skin so that the problem of thermal bridging is avoided. The design of each facade is adapted to the scale and character of its context, that to Skeldergate being simple and repetitive and whilst the Queen's Staithe front has a two storey high order and a play upon symmetry in response to the size of the adjoining buildings and to the views from the Ouse Bridge and the opposite river bank.

The concrete structure is exposed in the ceilings of the office space to provide sufficient thermal mass to avoid summer overheating as a part of the 'selective' approach to environmental control which it adopts (Hawkes, 1981). Another aspect of this is the clear differentiation in the operational mode between summer and winter. The aim of this is for the building to be 'free-running' in summer by using its form and fabric to modify the ambient environment to provide satisfactory internal conditions (Humphreys, 1978). In winter the windows would be locked shut and a mechanical heating and ventilating system would allow solar gains through the arcade to be captured to contribute to the heating requirements and for waste heat from office equipment and the occupants of the building to be recovered further to reduce the heating load. Similar principles would also apply to the rehabilitated block. In both cases the glazed arcade would provide an 'intermediate' environment, with temperatures in winter at a point between ambient and that in the surrounding heated spaces. This has the effect of avoiding the extremes of the English climate and can thus promote a use of the public domain, for pavement cafes for example, which is usually severely restricted.

Technical analysis

The atrium has enjoyed a recent popularity as an architectural feature, and is often associated with energy saving. However, it would probably be fair to say that most existing atria, many of which are heated, cooled, mechanically ventilated, and even on some occasions artificially lit during daylight hours, consume far more energy than they save.

Before describing the analytical procedure used to evaluate the thermal performance of this particular building, with its unheated arcade, it is appropriate to ask the question - what is the difference between an atrium (or arcade) building, and simply a deep-plan building with a glazed roof? To answer this, let us consider the conceptual origin of the covered court - the covering over of an otherwise open space.

This open space, the court or on a smaller scale the lightwell, would provide daylighting to the rooms facing the court to a depth of up to about 6m, and also natural ventilation, both single-sided and cross ventilation. At times of good weather, the court could also be a pleasant amenity space. On glazing over the courtyard, we would argue, there should be no loss of these functions. First, this will require a highly light-transmitting roof and wall surfaces of high reflectance. Secondly, it will require a controlled access to fresh air, small amounts in winter, but large amounts in summer.

Assuming both of these conditions can be met, let us now consider the extra advantages the enclosure would bring. The most striking is the thermal effect on the winter climate of the court. The temperature will be elevated considerably due to heat gains through the walls from the heated building, and depending on the geometry, solar gains. (In the absence of the roof, these gains would be convected away almost instantly and the improvement to the climate would be negligible). This increase in temperature subsequently has the effect of reducing heat losses from the heated building to the court, thereby saving energy. It also makes the court far more habitable, although remaining unheated. Both of these effects are considerable as the quantitative analysis will show. Other important improvements to winter habitability are, of course, absence of rain, snow and wind.

Summer conditions could also be improved, since the roof provides a structure upon which to support shading devices. This enables the whole of the court to be shaded and, in conjunction with generous ventilation openings, will result in lower environmental temperatures than in the uncovered court. As illustrated in Figure 8, it also provides stack ventilation to the surrounding rooms, particularly valuable in conditions of low wind-speed, and effective for structural cooling at night-time.

In contrast, a deep-plan building will offer none of these possibilities except, perhaps, daylighting on the top floor. It will, of course, provide a greater floor area, but the value of this must be weighed against the extra servicing costs, and the loss of the courtyard as an amenity together with the psychological disadvantage of the deep-plan spaces.

Thermal evaluation

We have used the model ATRIUM, described by Baker (1983c), to investigate the thermal performance of the proposed buildings.

The model is not a full dynamic simulation. This would require detailed input data, some of which would be unavailable at this stage in the design. ATRIUM is a modified steady-state model for use at an early stage in the design. It uses monthly average climatic data, and incorporates correction factors as published by the CIBSE for the degree-day method. Its most important feature is that it models the atrium (conservatory or arcade) by means of a resistance network, thereby showing the effect of varying the conductance and area of the walls separating the atrium from the heated building. It also accounts for the transfer of air between the atrium and the heated part of the building in a number of alternative modes. Direct gains to the heated part of the building are calculated using a solar/load ratio curve, after Balcombe and McFarland (1979).

Both the existing building with the retrofit arcade and the new building were modelled, and the results are summarized in Figures 9 and 10 respectively.

For the retrofit case, the graph shows the average monthly temperatures occurring in the arcade, compared with the ambient temperature. Note that there is a considerable elevation of temperature, between 5 and 7 degrees. Since we are considering monthly average values, and not actual values which are likely to vary quite widely, it is appropriate to introduce the idea of a 'seasonal shift' of the arcade 'climate'. The graph indicates a shift from January to May, brought about by the covering of the space.

When considering the habitability of the arcade, it must be remembered that the temperatures shown are monthly averages. Daytime temperatures during occupancy will be higher due to three factors: (i) the ambient temperature is above average, (ii) the heated part of the building is up to the set point, and (iii) solar radiation when available will all occur in this period. Simulation results indicate that the elevation above the average on a sunny winter day is likely to be between 4 and 7°C and on a cloudy day between 2 and 4°C.

The bar chart shows the energy consumption of the whole building for three different situations. The base case is for the existing building with no arcade, and shows a useful

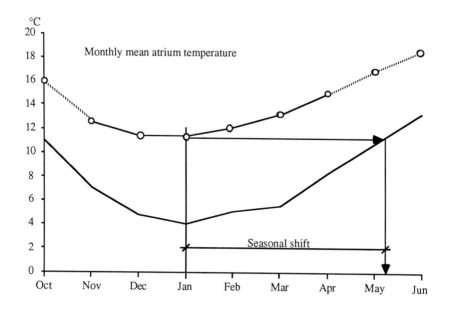

Monthly mean atrium temperature

Seasonal shift

Annual useful heat demand

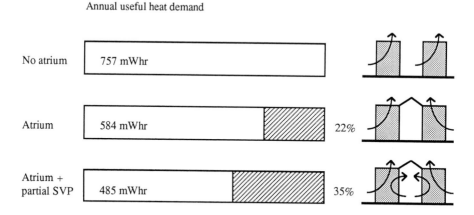

No atrium   757 mWhr

Atrium   584 mWhr   22%

Atrium + partial SVP   485 mWhr   35%

Casual gains 15 W/m2

Figure 9   *Results of atrium analysis: existing block*

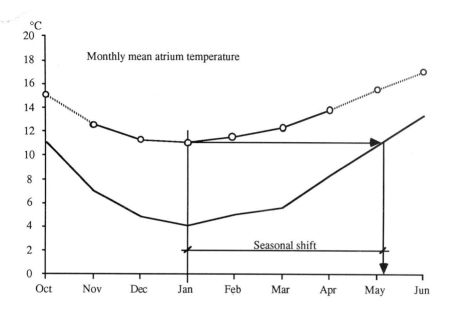

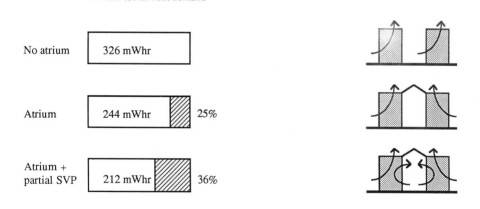

Figure 10 *Results of atrium analysis: new block*

heat demand of 757 mWhr per annum. Simply covering over the open space would reduce this by 22% to 584 mWhr per annum, whilst the use of the arcade to provide pre-heated ventilation to the rooms facing the arcade reduces the heat demand further to 485 mWhr, a total reduction of 35%.

The results for the new building are quite similar. This is due to the similarity in the shape and proportion of the two arcades, and also the effect of double glazing to the inner court is compensated by a greater area of glazing (48% compared with 25% for the existing building).

The results of the thermal analysis show that in both cases the arcades significantly reduce energy consumption of the adjacent building, and greatly increase the amenity value of the space between the buildings.

Conclusion

The aim of this paper has been to present two arguments, one to do with the methodology of architectural and urban studies, the other specifically about developments in urban form in response to the need to reduce energy consumption.

Leslie Martin (1967) has suggested that the aim of architectural and urban studies is "... to study the potentialities of the built form ... of setting out the choices in building an environment". Implicit in this proposition is the need to establish a relationship between the worlds of research and practice. This is not to suggest that such research is restricted to the solutions of specific problems arising in practice - so called 'fire-brigade' research, but that it operates within an appreciation of and engagement with the wide concerns of practice. The review of Cambridge research with which we began aimed to show how theory and practice have evolved hand-in-hand over a period of twenty years. The design described here would not have been possible if the research had not taken place. On the other hand, the continued development of the research depends upon the test of application in practice, where the general is made specific.

Turning, finally, to the question of the architecture of the low-energy city, the proposition which underlies the work presented here is that the development of an understanding of the physics of glazed court spaces within the buildings in the British climate suggests the possibility of an interesting development in the morphology of the city. Glazed spaces of this kind permit the construction of buildings which offer considerable energy savings when compared with the fully air-conditioned designs of much recent and current practice. (There are also potential savings in initial construction costs). In addition they create protected public open spaces of considerable environmental and commercial attraction. If the principles of atrium building design are extended to the redevelopment of areas in the centre of cities, through a combination of new buildings and the rehabilitation of existing city blocks, the possibility emerges of developing a network of glazed pedestrian routes which may be superimposed upon the existing street pattern, opening up the centre of the block which has traditionally been relegated to secondary functions and, hence, of offering a further element of choice in building a setting for a more rewarding urban life.

References

The Architects' Journal (1985). A riverside development at York. *AJ*, Vol. 182, No. 40, pp. 35-40.

Baker, N. (1983a). Atria and conservatories 2: a case study 2. *The Architects' Journal*, Vol. 177, No. 20.

Baker, N. (1983b). Atria and conservatories 3: principles of design. *The Architects' Journal*, Vol. 177, No. 21.

Baker, N. (1983c). The thermal performance of large glazed spaces. *Conference Proceedings of the CEC Solar Architecture Conference, Cannes, 1982*. American Solar Energy Society.

Balcombe, J.D. and McFarland, R. (1979). A simple empirical method for estimating the performance of a direct gain passive solar heated building. *Proceedings of the Third National Passive Conference, San Jose, California, 1979*. Newark, Delaware: American Section, International Solar Energy Society, Inc.

Geist, J.F. (1983). *Arcades: the History of a Building Type*, (English edition). Cambridge, Mass.: MIT Press.

Greenberg, S. and Hawkes, D. (1986). Commended design, York Riverside Competition. *The Architects' Journal*, Vol. 183, No. 16, p. 52.

Hawkes, D. (1981). Building shape and energy use. In D. Hawkes and J. Owers (eds.), *The Architecture of Energy*. Harlow: Construction Press, Longmans.

Hawkes, D. (1983). Atria and conservatories 1: introduction and case study 1. *The Architects' Journal*, Vol. 177, No. 19.

Hawkes, D. and MacCormac, R. (1978). Office form: energy and land use. *RIBA Journal*, (June).

Humphreys, M. (1978). *Outdoor Temperatures and Comfort Indoors*. Current Paper 53/78. Garston: Building Research Establishment.

Macleod, R. (1971). *Style and Society: Architectural Ideology in Britain: 1835-1914*. London: RIBA Publications.

Martin, L. (1967). Architect's approach to architecture. *RIBA Journal* (May).

Martin, L. (1972). The grid as generator. In L. Martin and L. March (eds.), *Urban Space and Structures*. Cambridge University Press.

Martin, L. *et al.* (1972). Speculations. In L. Martin and L. March (eds.). *Urban Space and Structures*, Cambridge University Press.

Martin, L. and March, L. (1966). Land use and built forms. *Cambridge Research* (April).

Matthews, L. (1984). The potential for solar heating in central urban areas: a case study. In *Proceedings of First E.C. Conference on Solar Heating*, Amsterdam.

Matthews, L. (1985). *Energy Conservation in Central Urban Buildings*. Doctoral dissertation, University of Cambridge.

Scott, G. (1914). *The Architecture of Humanism: a Study in the History of Taste*. London: Constable and Co.

LOW ENERGY TERRACE HOUSING PROJECT: GALLERIA 'ZUR LINDE'

Martin Wagner
Sud California Istituto d'Architettura
Vico Morcote, Switzerland

This terrace housing project, designed by H.R. Spycher & Sons and Martin Wagner, is located in Schmitten, Canton of Fribourg, Switzerland. It is situated on a south-facing slope between a highway at the bottom of the slope and a subdivision road at the top of the hill. This road gives access to the project for people arriving by car, while pedestrians, coming from the nearby train station or from the town of Schmitten, arrive from below.

There are, therefore, two main entrances to the central covered pedestrian street (the Galleria), one at the top and the other at the foot of the hill. Twelve houses have entrances located inside the galleria which serves in winter as a greenhouse and airlock; while the two front houses, with their loggia façades facing southwards, have entries located in the portico behind the 'city gate'.

Since the view towards the south overlooking the valley is marred by a railway yard, industrial warehouses and a huge grain silo, it was decided to build the fourteen houses and their garden sheds on seven terraces with their plans running parallel to the contour lines, giving them an undisturbed eastern and western view to the Alps or Jura Mountains. Two units sit on a terrace and each unit comprises four bedrooms, three baths, living room, dining room, kitchen, mechanical room and cellar. Their longitudinal and mirrored plans are connected with arches and a glass roof across the central street. All bathrooms, kitchens, stairs and circulation spaces are placed in the centre of the plan with a skylight facing south, allowing light and energy to penetrate all three storeys.

This passive solar energy as well as the air-exchange of the houses are collected by a ventilation system connected to a 2.5 kW heat pump which keeps the room temperature at 20°C when the outdoor temperature is -10°C. This extremely low energy consumption is due not only to the new heat-exchange technology but also to the form of the plan with minimum outside surface, and the urban form of the 'Siedlung'.

Street elevation

Garden elevation

North facade

South facade

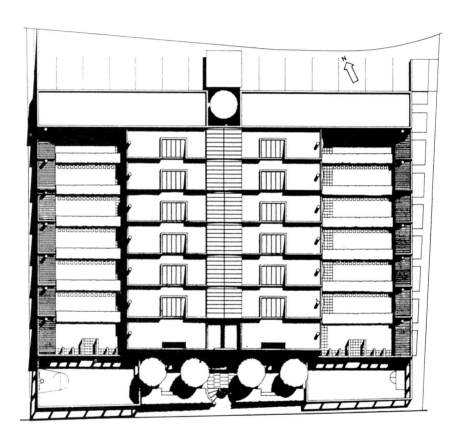

Roof plan

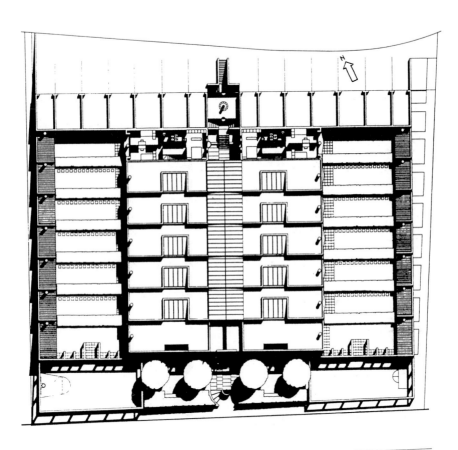

Plan level 8

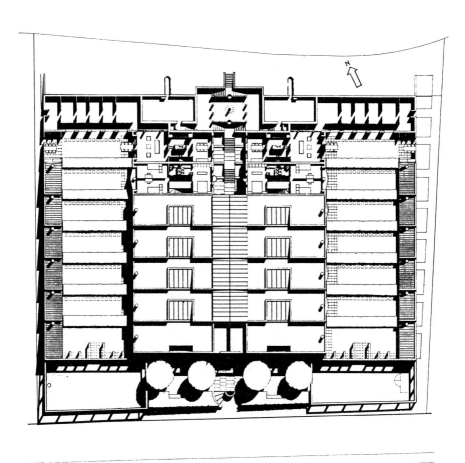

Plan level 7

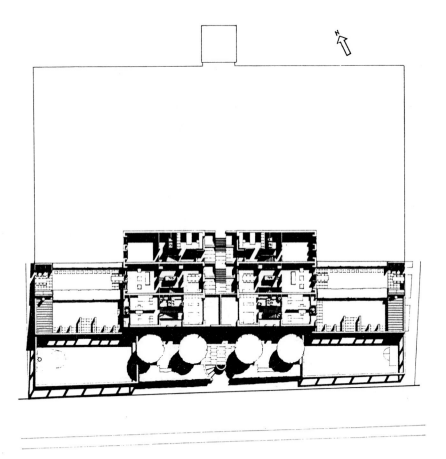

Plan level 2

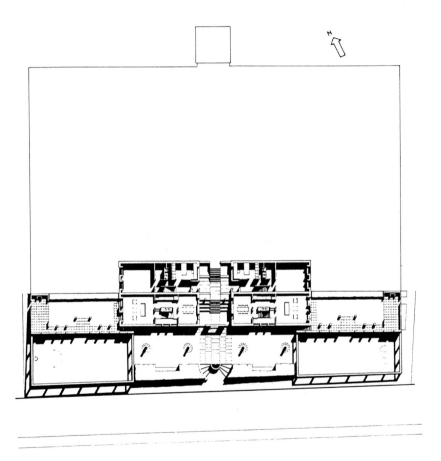

Plan level 1

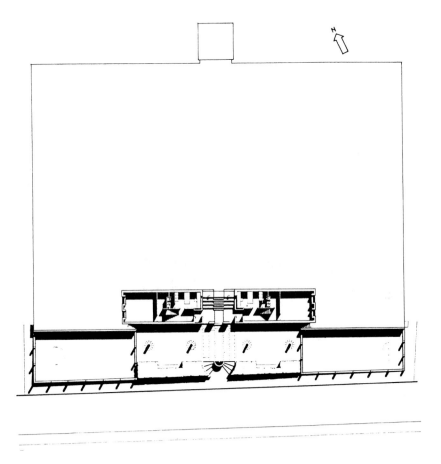

Plan level 0

SEMINAR PARTICIPANTS

Dr Nicholas Baker
The Martin Centre for Architectural and Urban Studies
University of Cambridge, England

Dr Tomas de la Barra
Instituto de Urbanismo
Universidad Central de Venezuela, Caracas

Dr Mark Barrett
Energy Research Group
The Open University, Milton Keynes, England

Mr Hugh Barton
Department of Town and Country Planning
Bristol Polytechnic, England

Dr Frank Brown
Centre for Configurational Studies
The Open University, Milton Keynes, England

Dr Ian Cooper
Eclipse Research Consultants
Cambridge, England

Prof Albert Dupagne
Laboratoire d'Etudes Méthodologiques Architecturales
Université de Liège, Belgium

Mr Malcolm Fergusson
Earth Resources Research Ltd.
London, England

Prof Vinod Gupta
School of Planning and Architecture
New Delhi, India

Mr Geoffrey Hammond
Applied Energy Group, School of Mechanical Engineering
Cranfield Institute of Technology, England

Dr Dean Hawkes
The Martin Centre for Architectural and Urban Studies
University of Cambridge, England

Dr Barry Hutt
W.S. Atkins and Partners
Epsom, England

Prof Sergio Los
Istituto Universitario di Architettura di Venezia
Italy